Stories for Mormons

Selected and Edited by
Rick Walton and Fern Oviatt

BOOKCRAFT
Salt Lake City, Utah

Library of Congress Catalog Card Number: 83-72685
ISBN O-88494-508-1

2 3 4 5 6 7 8 9 10   89 88 87 86 85 84 83

Lithographed in the United States of America
PUBLISHERS PRESS
Salt Lake City, Utah

Preface

Stories have always had a way of reaching people that simple statements of fact or opinion have not. Teachers throughout the ages have used the story as an effective method of teaching and touching their students. Even Christ, the greatest teacher of all, taught through stories. And surely, for personal reading and enjoyment, the story is the age-old favorite.

Not far behind the story in popularity is the short verse that conveys a principle, a concept, a feeling. This format brings us distilled and focused wisdom in an appealing pattern that helps in the retention and the retelling of the message.

This book is a collection of stories and verse that convey powerful and timeless messages. Where the authors could be determined, we have given them credit for their works. For many of the stories and some of the poems, however, this information could not be obtained, since they have passed from speaker to listener for years and the identity of their originators has been lost. To all sources, whether named or not, we express our appreciation.

Special thanks to Ann Walton for her considerable help in various aspects of this book.

Contents

Adversity and Contention

THE ART OF QUARRELING

Two old men lived in the same room, and had never disagreed.

One of the men said, "Let's just have one quarrel, like other men."

The other replied, "I don't know how to quarrel."

Said the first, "Here, I'll put a brick between us, and say that it's mine. You then say that it's not mine and then we'll fight over that."

But when they had put the brick between them the first said, "It's mine, and not yours."

"If it's yours," said the second man, "then take it."

And the two men were never able to succeed at quarreling.

CROSSING THE BRIDGE

There was once a man and a woman who set out one morning to visit a friend's house some distance from their own. They had not gone very far before the woman remembered a bridge they would have to cross, which was very old and was said to be unsafe. She immediately began to worry about it.

"What will we do about the bridge?" she said to her husband. "I don't dare go over it, and we can't cross the river any other way."

"Oh," said the man, "I forgot about that bridge. It's a bad place. What if it breaks through and we fall into the water and drown?"

"And what if," said the wife, "you step on a rotten plank and break your leg? What would become of me and the baby?"

"I don't know," said the man. "What would become of any of us? I couldn't work, and we would all starve to death!"

So they went on worrying until they got to the bridge, and, lo and behold, they saw that since they had been there last, a new bridge had been built, and they crossed over it in perfect safety, and found they might have spared themselves all their anxiety.

DOESN'T MIND FALLING

In the park, a little girl was learning to skate by a sort of trial and error method, and experiencing falls in the process. She was resting from her labors when a boastful little boy skated up to her side and taunted, "I can skate better than you can."

"Yes, I suppose you can," the little girl agreed. "But," she added proudly, "I'll bet you mind falling down more than I do."

—*Christian Science Monitor*

DO-IT-YOURSELF WORLD

"The world is a looking glass, and gives back to every man the reflection of his own face." (William Makepeace Thackeray.)

I had to live a long time before I found the courage to admit to myself that we—all of us—make our own world. I take frequent trips to New York and I had decided that all New York cab drivers were impatient and bad-tempered. Hotel and railroad employees were the same. I found them all difficult to get along with.

Then one day in New York, I came upon the words from Thackeray quoted above. The very same day, when a cabbie and I were snarling at each other, this thought occurred to me: Could this whole situation be the result of my own outlook?

I began to live Thackeray's idea. On my next trip east, I encountered not one unpleasant taxi driver, elevator operator or railroad employee. Had New York changed or had I? The answer was clear.

To abandon excuses for one's own shortcomings is like journeying to a distant land where everything is new and strange. Here you have to assume the responsibility for failures or difficulties yourself. Of course, outside pressures do influence our lives, but they don't control them. To assume they do is sheer evasion. Since that day in New York, I've come to believe that this idea is the basis of all human relationships. The quickest way to correct the other fellow's attitude is to correct your own. Try it. It works. And it adds immeasurably to the fun of meeting people and being alive.

—*King Vidor*

THE HORSE AND THE DEER

A horse and a deer were grazing together on the prairie, when to their horror they saw in the distance a grass fire, the flames approaching rapidly.

"What can we do," said the deer, "to escape being roasted alive?"

Said the horse, "I know of only one way to escape. That is to meet the danger boldly." So saying, he rushed at top speed toward the advancing flames. In a single bound he leapt through the flames and landed beyond the danger.

The deer, terrified, fled in the opposite direction. The flames, licking at his heels, finally overtook him and he died miserably.

The horse later returned and found the body of his friend on the blackened plain. Pausing beside him, he thought, "My poor friend, your quickness proved your ruin, since you didn't have the courage to move in the right direction. How much better it would have been if you had boldly faced danger, rather than fleeing panic-stricken from unavoidable troubles."

—*Paul Peregrine*

HOW QUARRELS BEGIN

"I wish that pony were mine," said a little boy, who stood at a window looking down the road.

"What would you do with him?" asked his brother.

"Ride him, that's what I'd do."

"All day long?"

"Yes, from morning until night."

"You'd have to let me ride him sometimes," said the other.

"Why would I? You'd have no right to him if he was mine."

"Father would make you let me have him part of the time."

"No, he wouldn't!"

"My children," said their mother, who had been listening, and now saw that they were beginning to get angry with each other, and all for nothing, "let me tell you of a quarrel between two boys no bigger nor older than you are, that I read about the other day. They were going along a road, talking together in a pleasant way, when one of them said:

"'I wish I had all the pastureland in the world.'

"The other said, 'And I wish I had all the cattle in the world.'

"'What would you do then?' asked his friend.

"'Why, I would turn them into your pastureland.'

"'No, you wouldn't,' was the reply.

"'Yes, I would.'

"'But I wouldn't let you.'

"'I wouldn't ask you.'

"'You wouldn't do it.'

"'I would.'

"'You won't!'

"'I will,' and with that they seized and began hitting each other."

The children laughed, but their mother said, "You see in what trifles quarrels often begin. Were you any wiser than these boys in your half-angry talk about an imaginary pony? If I had not been here, who knows but what you might have been as silly and stupid as they were!"

THE KING AND THE SPIDER

The king of Scotland had been attacked by his enemies, had been beaten in several battles, was forsaken by nearly all of his friends, and knew that if he were taken he would at once be put to death. He was hiding in a cottage, and as he was walking in its garden, sadly thinking of his problems, he noticed a spider that was trying to get to the top of the garden wall. Just as it had almost reached the top, it fell to the ground. Immediately it began to climb again, and when it was almost to the top, fell again. The king, interested in the poor insect, watched on. A third time the spider tried, with the same success, and so on until the eighth. The eighth time it also fell in the same manner, but, not a bit discouraged, began the climb once more. And the ninth time it succeeded and reached the top of the wall. The king, inspired by the perseverance of the spider, set out with renewed determination, conquered his enemies, and enjoyed a long and peaceful reign.

LEARNING THE VOICE

A storekeeper had a dispute with a customer about a bill. The storekeeper said he would go to the law about it. The customer tried all means to keep him from doing so. One morning the customer decided to make one last attempt to solve the problem. He went to the storekeeper's house and asked the storekeeper's son if he was at home. The storekeeper heard and recognized the customer's voice and shouted out, "Tell that rascal I'm not home." The customer calmly said, "I'm sorry you're not in a good mood. Have a good day," and went away.

The storekeeper was struck with the meekness of the reply and, looking again into the disputed bill, found that the customer was right and he was wrong. He went to the customer and, after explaining the situation and apologizing, said, "I have one question to ask you. How were you able to bear my abuse with such patience?"

"Friend," said the customer, "I will tell you. I once had as hot a temper as you, but I recognized that it was wrong, and that I had to do something about it. I noticed that men in a passion always spoke loudly, and I thought that if I could control my voice I would be able to control my passion. I have therefore made it a rule never to let my voice rise above a certain level, and it is by carefully observing this rule that I have been able to control my temper."

LIGHTING HIS WAY

Pericles was such a patient man that he was hardly ever angered. There was another man who did nothing but yell at him, complain about him, and verbally abuse him. But Pericles ignored him. One night as Pericles returned home, the man followed him, insulting him all the way. When Pericles reached his home, it was dark, so he called his servant and told him to get a torch and help the fellow get home.

LOOK AROUND

A woman struggled through many difficulties without complaining or showing the least impatience. A friend of hers, who admired these virtues, one day asked her what her secret was.

"I can tell you my secret easily," replied the woman. "It consists in nothing more than making a right use of my eyes."

Her friend asked her to explain.

"In whatever state I am," said the woman, "I first of all look up to heaven, and remember that my principal business here is to get there. I then look down on the earth, and call to mind how small a space I shall occupy in it when I am to be buried. I then look abroad on the world, and observe how many there are who are, in all respects, more unhappy than myself. Thus I learn where true happiness is placed, where all our cares must end, and how very little reason I have to worry or complain."

LUXURY LOST

Napoleon, when about fifteen years of age, was attending a military school at Paris. He complained to the superintendents of the school about its arrangements. He said the students' lifestyle was too easy. It couldn't prepare them for the hardships of the military. He requested that several measures be taken to make life rougher for the military students. He chose what was painful over what was pleasant. And because of that he was able, in later years, to conquer many peoples who had lived lives of luxury. Not until he came up against armies that knew the same self-denial that he himself practiced was he defeated.

MAKING THE BEST OF WHAT COMES

An old farmer had just finished harvesting his crop of wheat and was planning on selling it the following day. During the night, however, he was awakened by shouts of, "Fire! Fire!"

He jumped from bed and rushed outdoors where he was met by the sight of his granary burning down. He rushed to the fire to see if there was any hope of saving some of the grain, but soon realized that the entire crop would be destroyed. He stood still for a moment, and then stretched out his palms toward the blaze and said, "To an old man a fireplace is always welcome."

MISLEADING

The tail one day quarreled with the head and, instead of being forced to follow all the time, insisted that it should take its turn in leading. Accordingly, the tail attempted to lead and wherever it went it tore itself up terribly. And the head, which was obliged to follow a guide that could neither see nor hear, also suffered.

—*Plutarch*

THE PEACEFUL SONG

Three natural philosophers go out into the forest and find a nightingale's nest, and forthwith they begin to discuss the habits of the bird, its size, and the number of eggs it lays; and one pulls out of his pocket a treatise of Buffon, and another of Cuvier, and another of Audubon; and they read and dispute till at length the quarrel runs so high over the empty nest that they tear each other's pages, and get red in the face, and the woods ring with their conflict. Out of the green shade of a neighboring thicket the bird itself rested and, disturbed by these side noises, begins to sing. At first its song is soft and low, and then it rises and swells, and waves of melody float up over the trees and fill the air with tremulous music, and the entranced philosophers, subdued and ashamed of their quarrel, shut their books and walk home without a word. So men who, around the empty sepulchre of Christ, have wrangled about religion until Christ Himself, disturbed by their discords, sings to them out of heaven of love and peace and joy in the Holy Ghost, are ashamed of their conflicts, and go quietly and meekly to their duties.

—*Henry Ward Beecher*

REPAIRING AN ACCIDENT

After the publication of his great work, the *Principia,* Isaac Newton turned his attention to chemistry, spending a long time studying it and writing out his observations and discoveries. One day while the philosopher was at church, his dog,

Diamond, turned over a lighted candle, which set fire to all the papers on which his work was written.

When Isaac returned and found the charred heap, he exclaimed, with admirable self-control, "Oh, Diamond, Diamond, you little know the mischief you have done!" But the philosopher's grief at the loss of his work is said to have affected his brain, for though he lived forty years after the accident, and published several editions of his works, he never made any more great discoveries.

In contrast, in 1821 the legislature of Louisiana elected Edward Livingston to revise the entire system of criminal law of the state. Accepting the commission, he took two years to prepare a code of criminal law in both French and English. He had given the final touches to the manuscript.

One night Mr. Livingston sat up until one o'clock to finish some of the work. He then went to bed, and in two or three hours was awakened by the cry of fire. He rushed to his writing room where the fire had broken out, to find his work reduced to ashes. He was greatly dismayed, but was outwardly serene. He soothed his wife and daughter, who were greatly distressed at the loss, and the night after the accident sat up until three o'clock working to reproduce the burnt code. He was then sixty years old, but in two years he had completed the reproduction of his great work, of which an English jurist said that it showed Livingston to be "the first legal genius of modern times."

A RUDE BOY

At the foot of a street stood a man with a hand organ. Ten or twelve boys gathered around him, more filled with mischievousness than courtesy. One less noble than the rest said to his friends:

"Watch, I'll hit his hat!"

And he did. Packing a snowball, he threw it so violently that the poor man's hat was knocked into the gutter. A bystander expected to see some manifestations of anger. The musician stepped forward and picked up his hat. He then turned to the rude boy, bowed gracefully, and said:

"And now I will play you a tune to make you happy."

Which do you think was the Christian?

SOCRATES' WIFE

Socrates did not make a very good choice of a wife. Her name was Xantippe, and she had a terrible temper. One day after she had poured forth all the abuse she could think of, Socrates went out and sat on the doorstep. His calm and quiet look only made her more angry, and in her rage, she ran upstairs and poured a bucket of water on his head. But at this annoyance Socrates just laughed, and said, "It's surprising that so much thunder would cause such a small rainstorm."

THE SUCCESS OF FAILURE

In 1776 Charles Abbot, a son of a barber, was attending the king's school in Canterbury, England. He was quite a favorite with the clergymen of the cathedral, who were his father's customers. Through their influence the boy hoped to be appointed as a chorister in the cathedral choir, a position that paid quite well.

Another boy was in the running for the position and friends of both pushed for their favorite candidate. But the other boy was obviously a better singer and when the time came to choose, the other boy was chosen. Charles was crushed.

Fifty years later the chief justice of England, accompanied by a friend, attended service in the Canterbury cathedral. When the service had ended he said to his friend, "Do you see that old man there among the choristers? In him you behold the only person I ever envied. When at school in this town we were candidates together for a chorister's place. He got it, and if I had gained my wish he might have been accompanying you as chief justice, and pointing me out as his old schoolfellow, the singing man."

It was Charles Abbot, the disappointed barber's son, then Lord Tenterden, who thus recalled his early failure. It sent him back to school and as a "poor scholar" to Oxford, where he worked hard and became very successful.

THAT WAS FOR MYSELF

An unselfish charity worker went out one day soliciting money to help feed the poor. She approached a man on the street who appeared to be well-to-do and began to explain her cause.

"Get out of my way, you beggar," he said, and he struck her hard on the cheek.

The woman stood unmoving, and looking quietly into the man's eyes said, "Well, that was for myself. Now what will you give me for the poor?"

A TOO FOND MOTHER

A teacher once found it necessary to give a student a bad grade. The student's mother, a very proud woman, stormed into the teacher's office, cursed him, slapped him, and stormed out.

A colleague of the teacher, dismayed, ran in and asked if he should have the woman brought back and punished.

"No," said the teacher. "Let her go. It is nothing but an instance of a mother's excessive fondness for her child."

YOU ARE DISCOURAGED

In this street of life, walking in the darkness of the shadow, hungry old Satan was out hunting with his dogs, the little imps of human weakness.

A man came walking through life's street.

Satan said to the little devil, with a bitter face, "Go, get him for me."

Quickly the imp crossed the street and silently and lightly hopped to the man's shoulder. Close in his ear he whispered, "You are discouraged."

"No," said the man, "I am not discouraged."

"You are discouraged."

The man replied this time, "I do not think I am."

Louder and more decidedly the little imp said again, "I tell you, you are discouraged."

The man dropped his head and replied, "Well, I suppose I am."

The imp hopped back to Satan, and said promptly, "I have got him; he is discouraged."

Another man passed. Again old Satan said, "Get him for me."

The proud little demon of discouragement repeated his tactics. The first time that he said, "You are discouraged," the man replied emphatically, "No."

The second time the man replied, "I tell you I am not discouraged."

The third time he said, "I am not discouraged. You lie."

The man walked down the street, his head up, going toward the light.

The imp of discouragement returned to his master crestfallen.

"I couldn't get him. Three times I told him he was discouraged. The third time he called me a liar, and that discouraged *me*."

—*Chicago Examiner*

BLACK BREAD

The black bread of sorrow
   Is acrid to the taste,
But he who would be nourished
   Cannot afford to waste;

The white bread of gladness
   Is made of frothy yeast,
A little goes a long way
   When taken at life's feast;

The black bread of sorrow
   Is neither fine nor light,
Yet it refines the spirit
   Far better than the white;

With toil enough to bless it
   Some even find it sweet—
The heavy bread of sorrow
   That is so hard to eat!

—*Carrie Ward Lyon*

CHOICE

Better a scar to show the arrow came
Than go through life unscathed by any mark;
Better the ashes eloquent of flame
Than have the spirit's hearth forever dark.

Better to lose than miss the chance of gain,
Better a broken than a rusted knife.
Better to know love, even as a pain,
Than meeting death, all unaware of life.

—*Elinor Lennen*

CLOSE TO OUR NEED HIS HELPING IS

The day is long and the day is hard,
We are tired of the march and of keeping guard;
Tired of the sense of a fight to be won,
Of days to live through and of work to be done,
Tired of ourselves and of being alone.
Yet, all the while, did we only see,
We walk in the Lord's own company,
We fight, but 'tis He who nerves our arm;
He turns the arrows that else might harm,
And out of the storm He brings a calm;
And the work that we count so hard to do,
He makes it easy, for He works too;
And the days that seem so long to live are His,
A bit of His bright eternities; and close to our
   need His helping is.

—*Susan Coolidge*

GOD MAKE ME BRAVE

God, make me brave for life: oh, braver than this.
Let me straighten after pain, as a tree straightens
   after the rain.
Shining and lovely again.
God, make me brave for life; much braver
   than this.
As the blown grass lifts, let me rise
From sorrow with quiet eyes,
Knowing Thy way is wise.
God, make me brave; life brings
Such blinding things.
Help me to keep my sight;
Help me to see aright
That out of dark comes light.

—*Author Unknown*

NOT MINE, BUT THINE

All those who journey soon or late
Must pass within the garden's gate;
Must kneel alone in darkness there,
And battle with some fierce despair.
God pity those who cannot say:
"Not mine, but Thine;" who only pray
"Let this cup pass," and cannot see
The purpose in Gethsemane.

—*Ella Wheeler Wilcox*

ON THE TWENTY-THIRD PSALM

In "pastures green"? Not always; sometimes He
Who knoweth best, in kindness leadeth me
In weary ways, where heavy shadow be.

And by "still waters"? No, not always so;
Oft times the heavy tempests round me blow,
And o'er my soul the waves and billows go.

But when the storm beats loudest, and I cry
Aloud for help, the Master standeth by,
And whispers to my soul, "Lo, it is I."

So, where He leads me, I can safely go,
And in the blest hereafter I shall know
Why, in His wisdom, He hath led me so.

—*Author Unknown*

OUT IN THE FIELDS WITH GOD

The little cares that fretted me,
I lost them yesterday
Among the fields above the sea,
Among the winds at play,
Among the lowing of the herds,
The rustling of the trees,
Among the singing of the birds,
The humming of the bees.

The foolish fears of what might pass,
I cast them all away
Among the clover-scented grass,
Among the new-mown hay,
Among the rustling of the corn,
Where drowsy poppies nod,
Where ill thoughts die and good are born—
Out in the fields with God!

—*Author Unknown*

PRAYER

I do not ask to walk smooth paths
Nor bear an easy load.
I pray for strength and fortitude
To climb the rock-strewn road.

Give me such courage I can scale
The hardest peaks alone,
And transform every stumbling block
Into a stepping-stone.

—*Gail Brook Burket*

WHAT'S THE USE?

What's the use o' folks a-frownin'
    When the way's a little rough?
Frowns lay out the road fur smilin'
    You'll be wrinkled soon enough.
        What's the use?

What's the use o' folks a-sighin'?
    It's an awful waste o' breath,
An' a body can't stand wastin'
    What he needs so bad in death.
        What's the use?

What's the use o' even weepin'?
    Might as well go long an' smile.
Life, our longest, strongest arrow,
    Only lasts a little while.
        What's the use?

—*Paul Laurence Dunbar*

WORRY

The world is wide
In time and tide,
And—God is guide;
Then do not hurry.

That man is blest
Who does his best
And leaves the rest;
Then do not worry.

—*Charles F. Deems*

Blessings and Gratitude

THE BRIGHT SIDE

Little Harry had one very marked character trait. He always looked on the bright side.

One day he was all excited, expecting his father home soon. Somebody else was expecting him too. His mother had prepared a delicious dinner for the three of them. Now they were just waiting for the train.

"There's the whistle!" said Harry, and he ran out the door and was down to the station in three minutes.

It seemed to Harry's mother that Harry was taking a long time to get home. She kept looking out the window but he didn't come. Finally she looked out again and saw Harry walking home alone.

"He didn't come. I waited until everyone was off," Harry said soberly. His mother's heart sank.

"I think there may have been some accident on the other train," she said slowly.

"Yes," replied Harry, his face brightening, to her surprise. "Yes, and he is so busy helping others that he forgot to send us word."

Harry's father came on the next train, but in her joy at his return, Harry's mother still remembered the lesson she had learned.

DON'T THANK THE CLOUDS

A lady asked a prominent philanthropist for help in raising an orphan boy that she had charge of. He donated liberally to the cause. The lady was very grateful and said, "When he's old enough I'll teach him to know and thank his benefactor."

"Stop," said the good man, "you're mistaken. We don't thank the clouds for giving us rain. Teach the boy to look higher, and thank Him who gives both the clouds and the rain."

GEORGE'S GRATITUDE

After the American colonies had gained their independence, the colonies, of course, were ecstatic. And in England, King George, who had been sadly beaten in the conflict, also decreed a day of thanksgiving for the restoration of peace to his long-disturbed country.

On hearing of the decree, a friend of the king said to the king, "Your Majesty has sent out a proclamation for a day of thanksgiving. For what are we to give thanks? Is it because Your Majesty has lost thirteen of the fairest jewels from your crown?"

"No, no," replied the king, "not for that."

"Shall we, then, give thanks that so many thousands of our fellowmen have poured out their blood in the struggle?"

"No, no," exclaimed George again, "not for that."

"For what, then, may it please Your Majesty, *are* we to give thanks?"

"Be thankful," said the king, "that it wasn't any worse."

GLAD TO SEE EACH OTHER

Two old men who had long been political opponents both became blind towards the end of their lives. On one occasion the two were brought together at a party. One of them said to the other, "Sir, you and I have been at odds, but I don't believe there are two persons in the world who would be more glad to see each other."

HOW TO BE CONTENT

A person should always consider how much more he has than he wants, and how much more unhappy he might be than he really is. When Aristippus was consoled for the loss of a farm, he replied, "Why, I still have three farms, and you only have one. So I ought to be more sorry for you than for me."

After the death of his brother, who left him a large fortune, Pitacus was offered a great amount of money by the king of Lydia to help console his grief. Pitacus thanked the king for his kindness but he told him he already had twice as much as he knew what to do with.

Bion, the philosopher, had a famous saying: "No man has so much worry as he who chases after happiness."

A story is told of an honest Dutchman, who, upon breaking his leg by falling from a tree, told those who rushed to his aid, "I'm thankful it was not my neck."

An old philosopher had a temperamental wife, who, after her display of temper before company, explained to his friends, "She has her good points. And if this is the worst of our troubles, I am a truly happy man."

If contentment does not bring riches, it at least banishes the desire for them. It destroys all unnecessary ambition, and certainly does not lead to corruption. It makes conversation sweet and thoughts peaceful.

IT MIGHT BE WORSE

The Arabs have a custom of thanking God that it is no worse. If one loses an eye, he thanks God it was not both eyes. If he loses a hand, he thanks God it was not both hands.

The habit of looking at the best side of every event is better than a man's weight in gold. When Fenelon's library was on fire, he exclaimed, "God be praised that it is not the home of some poor man!"

PLANTING APPLE TREES

A poor old man, busy planting apple trees, was interrupted by a passerby.

"Why do you plant trees when you know you won't be around to eat their fruit?"

The old man raised himself up and, leaning on his spade, replied, "Someone planted trees for me before I was born and I have eaten their fruit, so I show my gratitude by planting for others."

A QUART A DAY

There once was a sick man to whom a kind gentleman gave a quart of milk a day. At last the sick man died and the gentleman took it for granted that the milk delivery would also end. But soon after the man's death, the gentleman went to visit his widow. "I must tell you, sir," she said to him, "my husband has made a will, and has left the quart of milk to his brother."

A QUARTER A DAY

There once was a beggar who received a quarter every day from a gentleman. One day the gentleman was sick and did not go out. The next day, when he was able to go out again, he again passed the beggar and gave him a quarter. The ungrateful beggar quickly spoke up, "But sir, you owe me a quarter for yesterday too."

THANKSGIVING STREET

A man was complaining to a friend about his trials and difficulties. After a while the complaining became too much for the friend. "I see you have been living on Grumbling Street. I lived there myself for some time and never enjoyed good health. The air was bad, the house bad, the water bad; the birds never came and sang in the streets, and I was quite gloomy and sad. But I moved. I found myself a house on Thanksgiving Street and ever since I have had good health, and so have my family. The air is pure, the water pure, the house good. The sun shines on it all day, and I am as happy as I can be. Now I recommend that you move too. There are plenty of houses available on Thanksgiving Street and I'm sure you'd find yourself to be a new man. And I'd be glad to have you as a neighbor."

THAT WILL BE THANKING ME

An old man was taking his grain to the mill in sacks thrown across the back of his horse, when the horse stumbled and the grain fell to the ground. He didn't have the strength to raise it, but he saw a man riding along, and thought to ask him for help. However, he couldn't muster the courage to ask. The man, though, was a gentleman, and, not waiting to be asked, he dismounted, and between them they lifted the grain to the horse's back. The old man lifted his cap and said, "Sir, how will I ever thank you for your kindness?"

"Very easily," replied the man. "Whenever you see another man in the same condition as you were in just now, help him, and that will be thanking me."

—British Workman

WHAT COULD I POSSIBLY USE?

A very haughty man was approached by a missionary who began to talk to him about the blessings of the gospel. The man laughed, and said, "What blessings could I possibly use? I'm wealthy, I have my health, I have power, I'm respected—what else could your gospel give me?"

"A grateful heart," said the missionary.

WHAT DO POOR FOLKS DO?

A poor widow, not having blankets to shelter her son from the snow which was blown through the cracks of her miserable hovel, used to cover him with boards. One night he said to her, smiling contentedly, "Ma, what do poor folks do these cold nights, that haven't any boards to put on their children?"

WHAT DO YOU WANT WITH MY LAND?

A gentleman had a board put up on a part of his land, on which was written, "I will give this field to anyone who is really contented."

When an applicant came he asked, "Are you contented?"

The calm, quiet answer: "I am."

The gentleman's reply invariably was, "Then what do you want with my land?"

YOU TOLD ME I WAS A MAN

I was asked to lecture in a town in Great Britain. The hall I was to speak at was six miles from the train station. After I'd disembarked from the train, I asked a man standing nearby if he knew where this hall was. He said he did and would be glad to take me there.

As we drove, I noticed that he sat leaning forward in an awkward manner, with his face close to the windshield. Soon he folded a handkerchief and tied it around his neck. I asked him if he was cold.

"No, sir." Then he placed the handkerchief around his face. I asked him if he had toothache.

"No, sir," was the reply. Still he sat leaning forward.

At last I said, "Will you please tell me why you sit leaning forward that way with a handkerchief around your neck if you aren't cold and don't have a toothache?"

He said very quietly, "The windshield of this car has a hole in it, and the wind is cold and I'm trying to keep it from you."

I said in surprise, "You aren't putting your face to that broken glass to keep the wind from me, are you?"

"Yes, sir, I am."

"Why do you do that?"

"Because I owe everything I have in the world to you."

"But I've never seen you before."

"Yes you have; you just don't remember. I was begging on a street corner and you sat down and talked to me and told me that I was a man and that I could be better than I was at the time. After you left, I decided that I could and would be a man. Now I have a happy wife and a comfortable home. I'd stick my head in any hole under the heavens if it would do you any good."

—J. B. Gough

BANKRUPT

One midnight, deep in starlight still,
I dreamed that I received this bill:
(_____ in account with Life):
Five thousand breathless dawns all new;
Five thousand flowers fresh in dew;
Five thousand sunsets wrapped in gold;
One million snowflakes served ice-cold;
Five quiet friends; one baby's love;
One white-mad sea with clouds above;
One hundred music-haunted dreams
Of moon-drenched roads and hurrying streams;
Of prophesying winds, and trees;
Of silent stars and browsing bees;
One June night in a fragrant wood;
One heart that loved and understood.

I wondered when I waked that day,
How—how in God's name—I could pay!
                                        —*Cortlandt W. Sayres*

————————

THE CALM OF SILENT THINGS

Let the sweet influence
Of all growing things penetrate my being
And heal the wounds about my Soul;
Let me lie close to their hearts
And hide my weary head beneath their tender
    shade;
Let the sweet movement of their waving stems
Soothe my tired nerves.
And let the dear field hold me within itself;
Let me hear its many thoughts,
That my understanding may be quickened,
For I would learn the peace and calm
Of all these silent things.
                                        —*Alice Sprague*

————————

CONTENT

I was too ambitious in my deed,
And thought to distance all men in success,
Till God came on me, marked the place, and said,
"Ill-doer, henceforth keep within this line,
Attempting less than others"—and I stand
And work among Christ's little ones, content.
                                —*Elizabeth Barrett Browning*

————————

FOR BEAUTY, WE THANK THEE

For all life's beauties, and their beauteous growth;
For nature's laws and Thy rich providence;
For all Thy perfect processes of life;
For the minute perfection of Thy work,
Seen and unseen, in each remotest part;
For faith, and works, and gentle charity;
For all that makes for quiet in the world;
For all that lifts man from his common rut;
For all that knits the silken bond of peace;
For all that lifts the fringes of the night,
And lights the darkened corners of the earth;
For every broken gate and sundered bar;
For every wide-flung window of the soul;
For that Thou bearest all that Thou hast made;
    We thank Thee, Lord!
                                        —*John Oxenham*

————————

GIVE US THIS DAY OUR DAILY BREAD

Back of the loaf is the snowy flour,
And back of the flour the mill,
And back of the mill is the wheat and the shower,
And the sun and the Father's will.
                                    —*Malthie D. Babcock*

————————

HE CARES

Oh, wonderful story of deathless love;
Each child is dear to that Heart above.
He fights for me when I cannot fight,
He comforts me in the gloom of night,
He lifts the burden, for He is strong,
He stills the sigh and awakes the song;
The sorrow that bows me down He bears,
And loves and pardons, because He cares.

Let all who are sad take heart again;
We are not alone in our hours of pain;
Our Father stoops from His throne above
To soothe and quiet us with His love.
He leaves us not when the storm is high,
And we have safety, for He is nigh.
Can it be trouble that He doth share?
Oh, rest in peace, for the Lord doth care!
                                        —*Susan Coolidge*

————————

I THANK THEE, GOD, FOR BEAUTY

I thank Thee, God, for lovely, transient things,
For luminous clouds and shining, crystal dew,
For quivering shadows and delicate smoke that
    wings
Its way across a sky ineffably blue.

I thank Thee, God, for vagrant, fragile flowers,
For ethereal forests etched in fairy frost,
For wandering dreams of enchanted ivory towers,
And far, faint echoes as of voices lost.

Others may thank Thee, God, for food and
    raiment,
For guidance along the narrow path of duty,
For power to meet their debts with full, just
    payment,
But let me thank Thee, God, for fleeting beauty.
                                        —*Ruth N. Potts*

————————

THE JOY OF GIVING

Somehow, not only for Christmas
But all the long year through,
The joy that you give to others
Is the joy that comes back to you;
And the more you spend in blessing
The poor and lonely and sad,
The more of your heart's possessing
Returns to make you glad.

—*John Greenleaf Whittier*

NOT IN VAIN

If I can stop one heart from breaking,
I shall not live in vain:
If I can ease one life the aching,
Or cool one pain,
Or help one fainting robin
Unto his nest again,
I shall not live in vain.

—*Emily Dickinson*

OUR FATHER'S WORLD

The ships glide in at the harbor's mouth,
And the ships sail out to sea,
And the wind that sweeps from the sunny south
Is sweet as sweet can be.
There's a world of toil, and a world of pains,
And a world of trouble and care,
But O, in a world where our Father reigns,
There is gladness everywhere.

The harvest waves in the breezy morn,
And the men go forth to reap;
The fullness comes to the tasselled corn,
Whether we wake or sleep.
And far on the hills by feet untrod
There are blossoms that scent the air,
For O, in this world of our Father God,
There is beauty everywhere.

—*Margaret Sangster*

PLAIN SERMONS

I saw a man—and envied him beside—
Because of this world's goods he had great store;
But even as I envied him, he died,
And left me envious of him no more.

I saw another man—and envied still—
Because he was content with frugal lot;
But as I envied him, the rich man's will
Bequeathed him all, and envy I forgot.

Yet still another man I saw, and he
I envied for a calm and tranquil mind
That nothing fretted in the least degree—
Until, alas! I found that he was blind.

What vanity is envy! for I find
I have been rich in dross of thought, and poor
In that I was a fool, and lastly blind—
For never having seen myself before!

—*James Whitcomb Riley*

THANK GOD

Thank God for life!
Even though it bring much bitterness and strife,
And all our fairest hopes be wrecked and lost,
Even though there be more ill than good in life,
We cling to life and reckon not the cost.
Thank God for life!

Thank God for love!
For though sometimes grief follows in its wake,
Still we forget love's sorrow in love's joy,
And cherish tears with smiles for love's dear sake;
Only in heaven is bliss without alloy.
Thank God for love!

Thank God for pain!
No tear hath ever yet been shed in vain,
And in the end each sorrowing heart shall find
No curse, but blessings in the hand of pain;
Even when he smiteth, then is God most kind.
Thank God for pain!

Thank God for death!
Who touches anguished lips and stills their breath
And giveth peace unto each troubled breast;
Grief flies before thy touch, O blessed death;
God's sweetest gift; thy name in heaven is Rest.
Thank God for death!

—*Author Unknown*

THANKS BE TO GOD

I do not thank Thee, Lord,
That I have bread to eat while others starve;

Nor yet for work to do
While empty hands solicit Heaven;
Nor for a body strong
While other bodies flatten beds of pain.
No, not for these do I give thanks!

But I am grateful, Lord,
Because my meager loaf I may divide;
For that my busy hands
May move to meet another's need;
Because my doubled strength
I may expend to steady one who faints.
Yes, for all these do I give thanks!

For heart to share, desire to bear
And will to lift,
Flamed into one by deathless Love—
Thanks be to God for this!
Unspeakable! His Gift!

—*Janie Alford*

A THANKSGIVING TO GOD FOR HIS HOUSE

Lord, Thou hast given me a cell
    Wherein to dwell,
A little house whose humble roof
    Is weatherproof.

Low is my porch, as is my fate,
    Both void of state;
And yet the threshold of my door
    Is worn by the poor
Who thither come and freely get
    Good words or meat.

All these, and better Thou dost send
    Me, to this end,
That I should render, for my part,
    A thankful heart.

—*Robert Herrick*

Earth and Nature

BEHOLD THE FOWLS OF THE AIR

Martin Luther had a quick eye to detect and read the lessons of nature. On a certain calm summer evening, he happened to be standing at a window when he observed a small bird quietly settle down for the night. "Look how that little fellow preaches faith to us all!" he remarked. "He takes hold of his twig, tucks his head under his wing, and goes to sleep, leaving God to take care of him."

THE COTTAGE

T. D. Harding, the artist, famous for his farm scenes, met a man who, having eyes, saw not. The artist, while out walking, saw a cottage made picturesque by leaving nature to work her own sweet will. Brambles, wild roses, honeysuckle, lichens, and mosses covered it. The artist asked permission of the owner, who was lounging at the door, to paint it. Receiving his consent, he said he would return early the next morning and begin his task. He was there a little after sunrise, to be met by the owner with a smirking smile of self-congratulation. "I've been up since daybreak getting the cottage ready for you," he said.

The painter was disgusted as he looked upon the cottage, transformed from its picturesqueness into a neat and carefully trimmed house. Every loose branch had been cut away, and the wild roses and honeysuckles all ruthlessly lopped. He did not paint that.

THE GLORIOUS SUN

Dr. Stanley Livingston and Louis Bonaparte, ex-king of Holland, were once fellow-passengers on a steamboat. Doctor Livingston was walking the deck in the morning and gazing at the rising sun, which appeared to him unusually attractive. He passed near the distinguished stranger and, stopping for a moment, said to him, "What a glorious object!" pointing gracefully with his hand to the sun. The ex-king agreed and immediately added, "And how much more glorious, sir, must be its Maker, the Sun of Righteousness!"

THE HAPPIEST SEASON

An old man was asked, "Which is the happiest season of life?"

He answered, "When spring comes and, under the influence of the gentle warmth of the atmosphere, the buds begin to show themselves and to turn into flower, I think to myself, 'Oh, what a beautiful season is spring!' Then when summer comes and covers the trees with thick foliage, when the birds are so happy in singing their pretty songs, I say to myself, 'Oh, summer is a fine thing!' Then when autumn arrives, and I see the same trees laden with the finest and most tempting fruits, I cry out, 'Oh, how magnificent is autumn!' And, finally, when the rude and hard winter makes its appearance, and there are neither leaves nor fruits on the trees, then, through their naked branches, I look upward and perceive, better than I could ever do before, the splendid stars that glitter in the sky."

KILLING QUAIL

One morning just a week after we had moved into our house on Seventh North, as I was leaving for work, I found a group of shouting, arm-waving boys gathered around the big fir tree in the front yard. They had sticks and stones, and in a state of high excitement were fiercely attacking the lowest branches of the tree, which hung to the ground.

"Why?" I asked.

"There's a quail in the tree," they said in breathless zeal. "A quail!"

"Of course," said I, "what is wrong with that?"

"But don't you see, it is a live quail, a wild one!"

So they just *had* to kill it. They were on their way to the old B. Y. High School, and were Boy Scouts.

Does this story surprise you? What surprised me was when I later went to Chicago and saw squirrels running around the city parks in broad daylight. They would not last a day in Provo.... We have taught our children by precept and example that every living thing exists to be converted into cash and that whatever would not yield a return should be quickly exterminated to make way for the creatures that do.... I have heard important Latter-day Saint leaders express this philosophy and have seen bishops and stake presidents teaching their reluctant boys the delights of hunting for pleasure.

The earth is our enemy, I was taught. Does it not bring forth noxious weeds to afflict and torment man? And who cared if his allergies were the result of the Fall, man's own doing, and could be corrected only when he corrects himself? But one thing worried me: If God were to despise all things beneath him, as we do, where would that leave us?

—*Hugh Nibley*
Intellectual Autobiography

LIFE IN THE MIDST OF DEATH

One day late in autumn, walking in a wild wood, I suddenly stood still. Around me was a vast forest, with its mighty and stupendous trees, covered with their varied and decaying foliage, ready to fall by the first breath of the wind and mingle with the dead leaves already on the ground. And it seemed to be the ruin of the world, as if nature in her most beautiful forms were coming to a close. But I stopped in the silence, and found there were living beings amid the solitude and dreariness. At intervals, in the distance, a cock crew, a sparrow chirped; there was the hoarse voice of distant crows, a horse neighed; soon there was the lowing of an ox, the barking of a dog, the bleating of a sheep, and a small bird rustled amid the brushwood and the leaves, while the cooing of a pigeon was heard from afar. And I was alone, as amid the falling columns and prostrate architecture of some ancient and perished city. So I thought, if life decays and is extinct in some forms, it shall survive in others, and those the more precious and the more important; there may be life in the midst of death, if we had but the eye to see it and the ear

to hear the melody; and if the world perishes like the seared leaves of the forest, there will be another to rise from its ruins in imperishable beauty and with incorruptible adornments; a righteous population shall inhabit the world. And as the shades of evening descended and darkness spread itself over the scene, my spirit was comforted.

—*James Stratten*

LINCOLN AND A BIRD

Abraham Lincoln, out walking one day with an aide, stopped at a little shrub and looked into it. He then stopped and put his hand down through the twigs and leaves, as if to take something out.

His aide asked, "What do you find there, Mr. Lincoln?"

"There's a bird fallen from its nest and I'm trying to put it back again."

THE LORD TAKES PLEASURE

Pushing my way through a very dense and tangled thicket in a lone and lofty mountain region of Jamaica, I suddenly came upon a most magnificent orchid in full blossom. It was the *Phajus Tankervilliae*—a noble plant crowned with a pyramid-like spike of lily-like flowers whose expanding petals seemed to be the very perfection of beauty. For ages, I thought, that beautiful flower had been growing in that wild and unvisited spot, every season "filling the air around with beauty," and had in all probability never met a single human gaze before. "Had, then, all that divinely formed loveliness been wasted for those generations?" I asked myself; and I immediately replied, "No. God Himself is satisfied with it, and the Lord takes pleasure in this work of His hands."

—*Philip H. Gosse*

NATURE AND MIRACLES

There is a legend that when God made the Red Sea, He so formed it that its waters should open whenever the rod of Moses was stretched over it. In other words, it was God's law in nature that that exception to common custom with those waters should take place.

OLD JIM

Old Jim was a big bay horse, homely but intelligent. One night he slipped his halter and presented himself at his master's bedroom window at about 2:00 A.M., where he rubbed his nose against the sash and whinnied until he woke Mr. Wampole, his owner. Mr. Wampole was angry. He had been up until midnight with a sick child and he wanted to sleep, but he got up and led the troublesome animal back to the stable, returned to bed, and was on the borderline between consciousness and dreamland when crash, went the window. This time Old Jim had poked his nose through a pane and the cold night air blew in. Mr. Wampole got up, put Jim in the stable and used some colorful words. Upon his return to bed he told his wife there would be peace the rest of the night. But it was not to be. For the third time Jim returned to the window, this time bringing part of the halter. Upon investigation, Mr. Wampole found in a back stable, behind the one in which Old Jim is kept, one of his horses, Jim's pulling partner, fallen and helpless. It was a narrow stall and he might have died before morning. By hard work Mr. Wampole pulled him around and got him on his feet. Then he went back to Old Jim's stall and stood looking at him.

"Well," he said, "that beats all!" And he took the rest of Jim's halter off and threw it behind the feed box.

"Old Jim," he said, "will never wear a halter again—he knows as much as a man."

SHOOTING TURKEYS

I took my gun with the intention of indulging in a little amusement in hunting turkeys.... It never occurred to my mind that it was wrong—that indulging in "what was sport to me was death to them"; that in shooting turkeys, squirrels, etc., I was taking life that I could not give; therefore I indulged in the murderous sport without the least compunction of conscience....

While moving slowly forward in pursuit of something to kill, my mind was arrested with the reflection on the nature of my pursuit—that of amusing myself by giving pain and death to harmless, innocent creatures that perhaps had as much right to life and enjoyment as myself. I realized that such indulgence was without any

justification, and feeling condemned, I laid my gun on my shoulder, returned home, and from that time to this have felt no inclination for that murderous amusement.

—*Lorenzo Snow*

TENNYSON AND VIOLETS

James T. Fields and the poet Tennyson were wandering on the moors about midnight, with no moon to light them, when suddenly the poet dropped on his knees, with his face to the ground.

"What is it?" said Mr. Fields, afraid a sudden faintness or sickness had come on.

"Violets!" growled Tennyson. "Violets, man. Down on your knees and take a good sniff; you'll sleep all the better for it."

THAT BIRD WILL NEVER SING AGAIN

A gentleman riding with his family in the country saw a beautiful bird. His son, about four years old, noticed it and watched it with great interest, listening to its beautiful song. The father thought the boy would like an even closer look at the bird, and leaving the carriage, raised the gun and shot it.

The little boy, his eyes swimming in tears, cried, "Father, that bird will *never* sing again!"

The father never afterwards had the heart to shoot a bird.

WELLINGTON AND THE TOAD

In an English garden one day a young boy was busy playing with something on the ground. A man rode up on a horse and asked, "What do you have there?"

"It's a pet toad I'm feeding, and they're going to send me away to school and the toad is going to die."

"Never mind," said the man. "Go to school. I'll take care of the toad for you." And he did.

The boy went away to school and soon received a letter from the man reporting on the well-being of the toad. The letter was signed "The Duke of Wellington."

WORDSWORTH'S STUDY

When a visitor at Rydal Mount asked to see the poet Wordsworth's study, the maid showed him a little room containing a handful of books lying about on the table, sofa, and shelves, and remarked, "This is the master's library, where he keeps his books; but," returning to the door, "his study is out of doors."

———————

ALL THINGS BRIGHT AND BEAUTIFUL

All things bright and beautiful,
All creatures great and small,
All things wise and wonderful,
The Lord God made them all.

Each little flower that opens,
Each little bird that sings,
He made their glowing colours,
He made their tiny wings.

The purple-headed mountain,
The river running by,
The sunset, and the morning
That brightens up the sky.

The cold wind in the winter,
The pleasant summer sun,
The ripe fruits in the garden,
He made them every one.

The tall trees in the greenwood,
The meadows where we play,
The rushes by the water,
We gather every day.

He gave us eyes to see them,
And lips that we might tell
How great is God Almighty,
Who has made all things well.
                    —*Cecil Frances Alexander*

———————

THE BIRTH OF THE FLOWERS

God spoke! and from the arid scene
Sprang rich and verdant bowers,
Till all the earth was soft with green—
He smiled; and there were flowers.
                    —*Mary McNeil Fenollosa*

———————

DESIGN

This is a piece too fair
To be the child of Chance, and not of Care.
No Atoms casually together hurled
Could ever produce so beautiful a world.
                    —*John Dryden*

———————

GIVE ME BUT EYES

Give me but eyes
To know the joy that lies
In common things:
A pale moth's velvet wings,
A fern-fringed pool,
Green mosses dripping cool,
The voice of rain,
The clouds in silver train,
Friendship of trees,
A meadow loud with bees:
To glimpse each glad surprise,
Give me but eyes.
                    —*Gertrude E. Forth*

———————

GO TO THE WOODS AND HILLS

If thou art worn and hard beset
With sorrows that thou wouldst forget,
If thou wouldst read a lesson that will keep
Thy heart from fainting and thy soul from sleep,
Go to the woods and hills. No tears
Dim the sweet look that Nature wears.
                    —*Henry Wadsworth Longfellow*

———————

I LIKE A REVERENT TOWN

I like a reverent town that sees
The sacredness of trees,
Acknowledging their right
To whisper half the night
And all the day to talk
Above a shaded walk.
I like a reverent town
That hews no tree trunk down,
But lets it stand to know
Sidewalks around can go,
As if: "I comprehend,
You were here first, my friend!"
                    —*Charles Divine*

———————

MIRACLES

I believe a leaf of grass is no less than the journey-
    work of stars,
And the pismire is equally perfect, and a grain of
    sand, and the egg of the wren,
And the tree-toad is a chef-d'oeuvre for the
    highest,
And the running blackberry would adorn the
    parlors of heaven,
And the narrowest hinge in my hand puts to
    scorn all machinery,
And the cow crunching with depress'd head
    surpasses any statue,
And a mouse is miracle enough to stagger
    sextillions of infidels.

                                    —*Walt Whitman*
                        From *"Song of Myself"*

―――――――

NATURE'S CREED

I believe in the brook as it wanders
From hillside into glade;
I believe in the breeze as it whispers
When evening's shadows fade.
I believe in the roar of the river
As it dashes from high cascade;
I believe in the cry of the tempest
'Mid the thunder's cannonade.
I believe in the light of shining stars,
I believe in the sun and the moon;
I believe in the flash of lightning,
I believe in the night-bird's croon.
I believe in the faith of the flowers,
I believe in the rock and sod,
For in all of these appeareth clear
The handiwork of God.

                                    —*Author Unknown*

―――――――

SIGNS

I hear you
Praying for a Sign.
Open your window;
Look, the dew
Lies there upon your grass
And mine.

Open your door.
Above that hill—
Beyond the trees,

Beyond the town—
The morning star hangs
White and still.
Open your eyes,
You fool, and see
One fern unfold,
One poppy bloom,
One golden ear
Of ripened corn;
One ruddy apple
On the bough;
One russet leaf,
One swallow's wing
Turn southward
Following the sun;
One snowy hill,
One cedar tree—
And do not prate of Signs
To me.

                                    —*Barbara Young*

―――――――

THIS IS MY FATHER'S WORLD

This is my Father's world,
And to my listening ears,
All nature sings, and round me rings
The music of the spheres.
This is my Father's world:
I rest me in the thought
Of rocks and trees, of skies and seas;
His hand the wonders wrought.

This is my Father's world,
The birds their carols raise,
The morning light, the lily white,
Declare their Maker's praise.
This is my Father's world:
He shines in all that's fair;
In the rustling grass I hear Him pass,
He speaks to me everywhere.

This is my Father's world,
O! let me ne'er forget
That though the wrong seems oft so strong,
God is the Ruler yet.
This is my Father's world:
The battle is not done;
Jesus who died shall be satisfied,
And earth and heaven be one.

                                    —*Malthie D. Babcock*

―――――――

THRIFT

I wonder that God can afford it:
Violets deep in the glen,
Seldom or never discovered
To eyes of adoring men.

I marvel that God is not thrifty:
Last night on the Tappan Zee,
At one in the morning His moonlight
Was spilled, molten silver, for me.
                    —*Earle Bigelow Brown*

WE PLOW THE FIELDS

We plow the fields, and scatter
The good seed on the land,
But it is fed and watered
By God's almighty hand;
He sends the snow in winter,
The warmth to swell the grain,
The breezes and the sunshine,
And soft, refreshing rain.

He only is the Maker
Of all things near and far;
He paints the wayside flower,
He lights the evening star;
The winds and waves obey Him,
By Him the birds are fed;
Much more to us, His children,
He gives our daily bread.

We thank thee, then, O Father,
For all things bright and good,
The seed-time and the harvest,
Our life, our health, our food.
Accept the gifts we offer
For all Thy love imparts,
And, what Thou most desirest,
Our humble, thankful hearts.
                    —*Matthias Claudius*

WHEN I HEARD THE LEARNED ASTRONOMER

When I heard the learned astronomer;
When the proofs, the figures, were ranged in
    columns before me;
When I was shown the charts and diagrams,
    to add, divide, and measure them;
When I, sitting, heard the astronomer,
    where he lectured with much applause
    in the lecture room,
How soon, unaccountable, I became tired and
    sick;
Till rising and gliding out, I wander'd off
    by myself,
In the mystical moist night-air, and from time
    to time,
Looked up in perfect silence at the stars.
                    —*Walt Whitman*

Faith

THE ALPHABET PRAYER

A shepherd boy out in the fields with the sheep on Sunday morning heard the bells ringing to call the people to church, and there came over him a longing to pray to God. But how was he to pray? He had never prayed before. He thought a moment, then he knelt down on the grass and put his hands together, as he had seen people doing in pictures and on old monuments, and began, "A...B...C...D..."

A gentleman on his way to church saw the boy kneeling with closed eyes and joined hands, heard him distinctly saying the letters of the alphabet, and wondered what he was doing. So he stopped and called to the boy in a kindly voice, "My lad, what are you doing?"

The boy looked up, "I was praying, sir."

"But what are you saying your alphabet for?"

"Oh, I don't know what to say in a prayer, but I wanted to ask God to take care of me, and to bless me, and to help me; so I thought I would just say all I did know, and He would put the letters together and spell them out, and understand what I mean."

ALWAYS LOOK UP

I was once hiking in the mountains with a guide. We came to a narrow goat-path that clung to a precipice. You had to hold on to the small bushes that grow out of the rock. One false step, one loose hold on a branch, and you'd be dashed to pieces. I looked into the precipice and said something to the guide about the depth.

"Yes," he said, "but never look down. Look up. Look up to the sky. If you look down, a hundred to one you will get dizzy and fall. If you look up, you never can. You'll be safe as long as you fix your eyes on the skies."

—*Dr. Neale*

DO YOU UNDERSTAND IT?

"I will not believe anything except what I understand," said a self-confident young man in a hotel one day.

"Nor will I," said another.

"Neither will I," chimed in a third.

"Gentlemen," said one who sat close by, "do I understand you correctly that you will not believe anything you don't understand?"

"I will not," said one, and so said each one of the trio.

"Well," said the stranger, "in my ride this morning I saw some geese in a field eating grass. Do you believe that?"

"Certainly," said the three unbelievers.

"I also saw the pigs eating grass. Do you believe that?"

"Of course," said the three.

"And I also saw sheep and cows eating grass. Do you believe that?"

"Of course," was again replied.

"Well, the grass which they had formerly eaten had turned to feathers on the backs of the geese, to bristles on the backs of the swine, to wool on the sheep, and on the cows had turned to hair. Do you believe that, gentlemen?"

"Certainly," they replied.

"Yes, you believe it," he said, "but do you understand it?"

They were silent.

FAITH OF A COAL MINER

In a coal mine in Newcastle there was a terrible explosion and seventy-six men were trapped. Rescuers tried frantically to save them, but they were too late. All seventy-six men had suffocated or starved. When the bodies were carried up out of the mine, seven young men were discovered in a cave separate from the rest. Among these was one whose daily reading of the Bible to his widowed mother gave her great comfort. After his funeral, a sympathizing friend went to visit her. While the widow showed him the Bible her son would read from, he pulled out a lantern that had been taken from the mine and showed it to the widow. It had been the son's lantern. In the darkness of the suffocating pit, with a little bit of pointed iron, the dying son had engraved on the box his last message to his mother, "Fret not, my dear mother, for we were singing and praising God while we had time. Mother, follow God more than I did. Joseph, be a good lad to God and mother."

THE FAITH OF CHILDREN

One of the early brethren had been under bond for several months awaiting trial on a charge of unlawful cohabitation. The court set a day for his trial and a list of witnesses was prepared.

On the appointed day this brother said good-bye to his family, expecting that he would be convicted and receive sentence immediately. On appearing at court, however, he found that through some oversight or blunder, no witnesses had been summoned and the case was postponed.

The man took the train home and on arriving at the station saw his two little boys waiting for him. On being asked why they came for him when he himself had not expected to return until after he had served a term in the penitentiary, they replied, "Oh, we fasted this morning and prayed to the Lord to bring you home tonight and we knew He would, so we came to meet you."

Their faith was quite different than that shown by an old woman who heard her minister speak of that faith which was sufficient to move mountains. She went home, pulled down her window blinds and then prayed to the Lord to remove a mountain from in front of her door. After praying for some time, she arose from her knees and peeped out from behind the blind and saw the mountain still in its place. "There," she exclaimed, "I knew it couldn't be moved!"

AN INDIAN'S FAITH

In the year 1865, my Grandpa King rented a farm on the Spanish Fork River bottoms, about three miles above the town of Spanish Fork. He moved his family up there to live for the summer. Soon after he had moved up there, one bright summer morning, just after sunrise, an Indian

came to the door and asked grandpa to give him some medicine, because he had a very sick papoose.

Grandpa said, "I don't have any medicine. Go to the store and get medicine. The store has lots of medicine."

The Indian looked very disappointed, and said, "You have medicine. I want it."

Grandpa said, "No, I don't have any medicine."

But the Indian persisted. "You have medicine. I want it. Store medicine is no good. My papoose is very sick."

Grandpa then asked him where his papoose was. The Indian went to the top of a hill next to the house, and returned instantly with his son. He brought him to the door and sat him on the step, a child about six years of age.

Grandpa looked at the boy and saw that he was very, very sick. He laid his hands upon his head and administered to him. After doing this he told the Indian that the papoose would get well.

The Indian asked him, "How many days?"

Grandpa hesitated a moment, and then replied, "He will be well in two days."

The medicine the Indian wanted was for grandpa to ask God to make his papoose well.

The Indian went away seeming very pleased. In two days he returned, bringing with him a nice, large duck as a present for grandpa.

Grandpa asked him if his papoose was well. He replied, "Papoose is very well."

—Millie Babcock

NAIVE VERSUS MATURE FAITH

A few years ago in Idaho, a young couple were married in the Idaho Falls Temple. After a strenuous wedding day, they set out for their honeymoon. They decided to drive some distance that night. They crashed into a bridge and the boy was killed. The family was grieved, of course, for none could understand why this young man, who had fulfilled a mission and was a fine Latter-day Saint, should be killed on his wedding night. His mother wrung her hands, and the bride was trying to blame herself, wondering just why it had happened. I don't know why it happened. God may have had a hand in it. I'm sure it wasn't to punish the mother or the boy. I think the easiest explanation might be that this boy drove when he was sleepy and tired, violating the rules of safe driving, and had to pay the price. At least, that's the explanation that you and I can profit from most and do something about in our own living.

My thought is this, that I think sometimes we Latter-day Saints have a sort of naive faith, a blind faith. We feel that if we live our religion in general, if we are pretty good Latter-day Saints in some particulars, we shall be blessed in all things. And I doubt that very much. I'm reminded of the verse in the Doctrine and Covenants which goes something like this: "There is a law, irrevocably decreed before the foundations of the earth, upon which every blessing is predicated. And when we receive any blessing from God it is by obedience to *that* law [that particular law] upon which it is predicated." If we want a safe trip we'd better not only pray, but drive carefully and follow the rules of the road.

—*Lowell L. Bennion*

THE PARABLE OF THE OWL EXPRESS

During my college days, I was one of a class of students appointed to do fieldwork as a part of our courses in geology.

A certain assignment had kept us in the field many days. We had traversed, examined, and charted miles of lowlands and uplands, valleys and hills, mountain heights and canyon defiles. As the time allotted to the investigation drew near its close, we were overtaken by a violent wind, followed by a heavy snow—unseasonable and unexpected—but which, nevertheless, increased in intensity so that we were in danger of being snowbound in the hills. The storm reached its height while we were descending a long and steep mountainside several miles from the little railway station at which we had hoped to take a train that night for home. With great effort we reached the station late at night, while the storm was yet raging. We were suffering from the intense cold, and, to add to our discomfort, we learned that the expected train had been stopped by snowdrifts a few miles from the little station at which we waited.

The station was but an isolated telegraph post; the stationhouse comprised but one small room, a mile away from the nearest village. The reason for the maintenance of a telegraph post at this point was found in the dangerous nature of the road in the vicinity, and the convenient establishment of a water tank to supply the engines. The train for which we so expectantly and hopefully waited was the Owl Express—a fast night train connecting large cities. Its time schedule permitted stops at but few and these the most important stations; but, as we knew, it had to stop at this out-of-the-way post to replenish its water supply.

Long after midnight the train arrived in a terrific whirl of wind and snow. I lingered behind my companions as they hurriedly clambered aboard, for I was attracted by the engineer, who, during the brief stop, while his assistant was attending to the water replenishment, bustled about the engine, oiling some parts, adjusting others, and generally overhauling the panting locomotive. I ventured to speak to him, busy though he was. I asked how he felt on such a night. I thought of the possibility—the probability even—of snowdrifts or slides on the track; of bridges and high trestles which may have been loosened by the storm; of rock masses dislodged from the mountainside; of these and other possible obstacles. I realized that in the event of accident through obstruction on or disruption of the track, the engineer and the fireman would be the ones most exposed to danger; a violent collision would most likely cost them their lives. All of these thoughts and others I expressed in hasty questioning of the bustling, impatient engineer.

His answer was a lesson not yet forgotten. In effect he said, though in jerky and disjointed sentences: "The lights illuminate a hundred yards or more. All I try to do is cover that hundred yards of lighted track. That I can see, and for that distance I know the road bed is open and safe. And," he added, "believe me, I have never been able to drive this old engine of mine so fast as to outstrip that hundred yards of lighted track. The light of the engine is always ahead of me!"

As he climbed to his place in the cab, I hastened to board the first passenger coach; and as I sank into the cushioned seat in blissful enjoyment of the warmth and general comfort offering strong contrast to the wildness of the night, I thought deeply of the words of the grimy, oil-stained engineer. They were full of faith—the faith that accomplishes great things, the faith that gives courage and determination, the faith that leads to works. What if the engineer had failed; had yielded to fright and fear; had refused to go on because of the threatening dangers? Who knows what work may have been hindered; what great plans may have been nullified; what God-appointed commissions of mercy and relief may have been thwarted had the engineer weakened and quailed.

For a little distance the storm-swept track was lighted up; for that short space the engineer drove on!

We may not know what lies ahead of us in the future years, nor even in the days or hours immediately beyond. But for a few yards, or possibly only a few feet, the track is clear, our duty is plain, our course is illuminated. For that short distance, for the next step, lighted by the inspiration of God, go on!

—James E. Talmage

SACRIFICING ALL

Sacrifices unquestionably are the rule for anyone coming great distances for the privilege of entering a temple of the Lord.

This is especially true among the Mexican members at the annual Lamanite conference in Mesa, Arizona, where the opportunity of entering the temple is the achieving of a much-cherished goal. When one of these conferences ends, the Mexican members begin saving their centavos in hopes of attending the next one. But the story of a little, elderly sister in the gospel who made the 1964 trip to Mesa will long be remembered.

The sister in the mission office in Mexico who had charge of collecting the funds and arranging passage for the members was surprised one day when one of the women members came into the office clutching the full sum necessary for the trip. When queried as to how she had raised this amount of money, she replied that she had sold her home.

The mission sister scolded her a little, saying that it was fine to be able to make the trip, but how and where was she going to live when she returned from Mesa.

This humble sister answered that for the short time that remained for her on this earth she could live in any little corner. But her heavenly home was of the utmost concern and importance to her!

—Norma Schofield

SIGNS AND MIRACLES

An elder, in the early rise of the Church, was asked for a sign by one of those bold individuals who speak for the crowd.

"What kind of sign would be the most convincing?" asked the missionary in a quiet and self-possessed tone.

"Oh, any physical demonstration. I'm told that old man Thompson, when he lived here years ago, had an arm put on that a machine had pulled off. Something like that would suit us." And the speaker took in the crowd with an incredulous grin.

"Will someone get me a large knife?" the elder asked.

A knife was produced from somewhere.

"Now," said the elder, addressing the spokesman, "strip your arm to the shoulder and I'll perform a miracle for you."

"What will you do?"

"Cut your arm off before this crowd, and put it back again."

"No, you won't," was the reply. And the wonder-seeker slipped away into the crowd.

THE SLEDGEHAMMER

I saw the other day a man attempting to split a rock with a sledgehammer. Down came the hammer upon the stone as if it would crush it, but it merely bounced, leaving the rock as sound as before. Again the ponderous hammer was swung, and again it came down, but with the same result. Nothing was accomplished. The rock was still without a crack. I might have asked (as so many are disposed to ask concerning prayer) what good could result from such a waste of time and strength. But that man had faith. He believed in the power of that sledge. He believed that repeated blows had a tendency to split that rock. And so he kept at it. Blow after blow came down, all apparently in vain. But still he kept on without a thought of discouragement. He believed that a vigorously swung hammer has great power. And at last came one more blow and the work was done.

THEY BELIEVE IN THE DIVINITY OF THE WORK

Some years ago, I took a leading educator who was attending the National Education Association meetings in Salt Lake City up one of our canyons. On the way this educator began to ask questions about the organization of the Church. He was given a rather complete explanation of the religious system with its various quorums of the priesthood and its different auxiliary organizations.

After a few moments of silence, the educator remarked, "That is the most wonderful organization I have ever known. Why," he added with earnestness, "if we had that system everywhere, we could revolutionize the world."

"I am not quite sure you could," I returned.

"Why not?"

"Simply because everyone would not accept with this system the one thing that gives it force and power for good."

"What do you mean?" he inquired.

It happened we were passing at the moment an electric power plant which stood at the mouth of the canyon.

"Let me make my answer to your question clearer by an analogy. You see that electric plant. Now let us suppose such a plant was built with its pipelines, its turbines, its poles and wires, its transformers, its lamps and other essential equipment. Suppose also that there was no waterpower available to turn into the pipes. What would be the use of all of your electric system?"

"It would be useless, of course," he returned, "but how does this analogy apply to the question at issue?"

"Right here: The inner strength of Mormonism comes from the free will service of its members in the cause. It offers to each and all opportunity to serve without other reward than that which comes to them in the form of increase of their talents and in spiritual self-development. Would people generally be ready to give their time and talents, to take on responsible positions in the Church, to sing in the choir, to go on missions, and otherwise to devote their lives in generous measure without thought of pay, with only love of the work of the Master?"

"I am afraid not," he replied.

"Then what would be the use of the organization I have explained?"

"What puzzles me," he responded, "is, how can you get people to do all this work without monetary compensation?"

"The reason is simple," I replied. "They believe in the divinity of the work."

—*Howard R. Driggs*

WALKING ON WATER

A man once traveled to a very hot and very backward country. While there he met a high official in that country who begged him to tell him about the land he came from. The traveler spoke about railroads and newspapers, factories and airplanes. At last the traveler happened to say something about ice skating, and the official would no longer listen. He said, "You have told me many strange things, but I was willing to believe them because you said them. But I never will nor can believe that water becomes hard enough to be walked on. If the whole world told me so, I would not believe it. I see that you're trying to deceive me and I'll listen to you no more."

DEPENDENCE ON GOD

Even as the needle, that directs the hour,
Touched with the loadstone, by the secret power
Of hidden nature, points unto the Pole;
Even so the wavering powers of my soul,
Touched by the virtue of Thy Spirit, flee
From what is earth, and point alone to Thee.

When I have faith to hold Thee by the hand,
I walk securely, and methinks I stand
More firm than Atlas; but when I forsake
The safe protection of Thine arm, I quake
Like wind-shaked reeds, and have no strength
   at all,
But like a vine, the prop cut down, I fall.

—*Francis Quarles*

GOD MAKES A PATH

God makes a path, provides a guide,
And feeds a wilderness;
His glorious name, while breath remains,
O that I may confess.

Lost many a time, I have had no guide,
No house but a hollow tree!
In stormy winter night no fire,
No food, no company.

In Him I found a house, a bed,
A table, company;
No cup so bitter but's made sweet,
Where God shall sweetening be.

—*Roger Williams*

HE CARES

Why so impatient, my heart?
He who watches over birds, beasts and insects,
He who cared for you while you were yet unborn,
Think you He will not care for you now that you
    have come forth?
O my heart, how could you turn away from the
    smile of your Lord and wander so far
    from Him?

—*Kabir*

LIFE

O Love triumphant over guilt and sin,
My Soul is soiled, but Thou shalt enter in;
My feet must stumble if I walk alone,
Lonely my heart, till beating by Thine own,
My will is weakness till it rest in Thine,
Cut off, I wither, thirsting for the Vine,
My deeds are dry leaves on a sapless tree,
My life is lifeless till it live in Thee!

—*Frederick Lawrence Knowles*

LIFE AND DEATH

So he died for his faith. That is fine,
    More than most of us do.
But, say, can you add to that line
    That he lived for it too?
In his death he bore witness at last
    As a martyr to the truth.
Did his life do the same in the past,
    From the days of his youth?
It is easy to die. Men have died
    For a wish or a whim—
From bravado or passion or pride,
    Was it harder for him?
But to live—every day to live out
    All the truth that he dreamt,
While his friends met his conduct with doubt
    And the world with contempt.
Was it thus that he plodded ahead,
    Never turning aside?
Then we'll talk of the life that he lived.
    Never mind how he died.

—*Ernest Crosby*

LINES WRITTEN IN HER BREVIARY

Let nothing disturb thee,
Nothing affright thee;

All things are passing;
God never changeth;
Patient endurance
Attaineth all things;
Who God possesseth
In nothing is wanting;
Alone God sufficeth.

—*Saint Theresa*
(Translated by
Henry Wadsworth Longfellow)

NATURE

As a fond mother, when the day is o'er,
    Leads by the hand her little child to bed,
    Half willing, half reluctant to be led,
And leave his broken playthings on the floor,
Still gazing at them through the open door,
    Nor wholly reassured and comforted
    By promises of others in their stead,
Which, though more splendid, may not please
    him more;
So Nature deals with us, and takes away
    Our playthings one by one, and by the hand
    Leads us to rest so gently, that we go
Scarce knowing if we wish to go or stay,
    Being too full of sleep to understand
    How far the unknown transcends the what
    we know.

—*Henry Wadsworth Longfellow*

OH YET WE TRUST THAT SOMEHOW GOOD

Oh yet we trust that somehow good
Will be the final goal of ill,
To pangs of nature, sins of will,
Defects of doubt, and taints of blood;

That nothing walks with aimless feet;
That not one life shall be destroyed,
Or cast as rubbish to the void,
When God hath made the pile complete;

That not a worm is cloven in vain;
That not a moth with vain desire
Is shrivelled in a fruitless fire,
Or but subserves another's gain.

Behold, we know not anything;
I can but trust that good shall fall
At last—far off—at last, to all,
And every winter change to spring.

—*Alfred Lord Tennyson*

ON THE SETTING SUN

Those evening clouds, that setting ray,
And beauteous tints, serve to display
Their great Creator's praise;
Then let the short-lived thing called man,
Whose life's comprised within a span,
To Him his homage raise.

We often praise the evening clouds,
And tints so gay and bold,
But seldom think upon our God,
Who tinged these clouds with gold.

—*Sir Walter Scott*

PROPHECY

Somewhere Beauty dwells, all undefiled,
For I have seen a rose unfold
At dawn,
And wonder grow
In the eyes of a child.

Somewhere Love shall live, all unafraid,
For I have seen a woman clasp Death's hand
At birth,
And pass into the shadows
Undismayed.

Somewhere Life shall live, beyond the blue,
For I have seen the veil wear thin
And fall apart—
And the face of God
Shine through.

—*Nellie B. Miller*

THE SEEKERS

One asked a sign from God; and day by day
The sun arose in pearl, in scarlet set,
Each night the stars appeared in bright array,
Each morn the thirsting grass with dew was wet.
The corn failed not its harvest, nor the vine.
And yet he saw no sign.

One longed to hear a prophet; and he strayed
Through crowded streets, and by the open sea.
He saw men send their ships for distant trade,
And build for generations yet to be.
He saw the farmer sow his acres wide,
But went unsatisfied.

One prayed a sight of heaven; and erewhile
He saw a workman at his noontime rest.
He saw one dare for honor, and the smile
Of one who held a babe upon her breast;
At dusk two lovers walking hand in hand;
But did not understand.

—*Victor Starbuck*

UNTO THEE

Not for the eyes of men
May this day's work be done,
But unto Thee, O God,
That, with the setting sun,
My heart may know the matchless prize
Of sure approval in Thine eyes.

—*Thomas Curtis Clark*

WAIT ON

To talk with God,
No breath is lost—
    Talk on!

To walk with God,
No strength is lost—
    Walk on!

To wait on God,
No time is lost—
    Wait on!

—*Dnyanodaya*

WITH WHOM IS NO VARIABLENESS, NEITHER SHADOW OF TURNING

It fortifies my soul to know
That, though I perish, truth is so:
That, howsoever I stray and range,
Whatever I do, Thou dost not change.
I steadier step when I recall
That, if I slip, Thou does not fall.

—*Arthur Hugh Clough*

Family

ALWAYS BEFORE MY EYES

A businessman was at a convention in a large town some distance from his home. On the first night there, a colleague of his suggested that they go out on the town and pick up some women. "I can't," said the businessman; "my wife is always before my eyes and I cannot be unfaithful to her."

———————

THE ART OF SAYING NO

I was sitting with a mother once, when her twelve-year-old boy sprang into the room, eager and impetuous. "Mother," he shouted, "can I go out swimming this afternoon? All the boys are going."

The mother quietly shook her head. "I'm sorry," she said, "but you can't go."

The boy straightened himself defiantly. "I will go," he said.

Instantly a look of reproof and command came into the mother's face and she silently looked her boy in the eyes.

He softened at once. "I want to go awfully," he said.

"I know," she answered gently, "but your father has decided that you are not a good enough swimmer to go into the water without him, and he can't go with you this afternoon."

The boy was plainly bitterly disappointed. He went and sat down on the porch for some time in silence. Finally he came in again.

"Mother," he said, "I don't believe Harry can go swimming either. If I can get him, can we go over to the Pelham Woods together?"

"Oh yes," answered his mother, "and there are cookies in the cookie jar. You can take some for both of you."

Tom's face grew brighter, he made a plunge for his mother and gave her a hug which mussed up her hair and wrinkled her blouse. "Mother," he said, "I love you."

"I love you too, Tom," she answered quickly. And then Tom dashed out of the room.

I have since watched other mothers to see what their methods of refusal were:

"No, you cannot."
"No, and don't you ask me again."
"No, and stop teasing."
"No, and go away."
"No, and when I say no, I mean no."

These forms of refusal were common in a number of families. I heard them repeatedly, always spoken in an irritated tone. I even heard one mother say, "No, and if you ask me again I'll whip you."

How could I show those mothers that they were mistaken?

I am sure that children can be taught that it is just as necessary to obey a pleasant no as a cross one, and it is so much easier for them when they are refused kindly. The spirit of contention is not aroused, and all they have to do is to bear the disappointment, whatever it may be, which alone is hard enough for their eager little hearts to endure. But if they love you and trust you, and you give them as much sympathy over their trouble as you would over a cut finger, for instance, you will be surprised at how easily they will obey.

"It is easy to mind Aunt Margaret," I heard a little girl of twelve say not long ago. "She says no just as pleasantly as she says yes."

Isn't it worthwhile for busy, preoccupied mothers to make it easy to mind them, as far as possible?

———————

A DEBT TO MOTHER

A woman was left a widow with one child. She had a small home and meager income. She took in washing for her principal support. One morning she called Clarence earlier than usual, saying, "Come, now, son, you will have to get up. We have a larger wash than usual today. It will require a lot of wood." Clarence made no complaint but dressed and went to the woodshed where he cut a woodbox full of wood. Then he wrote a note to his mother and placed it under her plate at the table. When they came to breakfast the mother found Clarence's note, which read as follows: "Mother owes Clarence fifty cents for cutting woodbox full of wood." The mother's countenance fell for a moment and then she went to her small earnings and found the half dollar, which she gave to Clarence.

There wasn't much said at the table that morning, but the mother thought a great deal as she worked throughout the day. The next morning Clarence found a note on his own breakfast plate: "Clarence debtor to mother for going down into the valley of the shadow of death to give him life—nothing. For board and lodgings nine years—nothing. For clothing, washing, and mending, nine years—nothing. Total—nothing."

—George F. Richards

THE END OF MY TROUBLES

A young bride said to her mother on her wedding day, "I am the happiest girl in all the world because I have come to the end of all my troubles," and the wise old mother answered, "Yes, my dear, but you don't know which end."

—Hugh B. Brown

FATHER, THE KING

George the Third, king of Great Britain, while playing with his children, was once interrupted by the entrance of some great dignitaries. They were not men of his own court; if they had been, no explanation would have been necessary, but rather they were ambassadors from abroad.

Just as these dignitaries entered, one child was mounted on the back of his father, the king, who was playing the part of a horse. The king took in the situation in a moment when he saw the ambassadors, and, rising to his feet, he approached them and asked the head dignitary, "Are you a father?"

"Yes," replied the nobleman.

"Then," said the king, "I need not explain to you what I am doing."

A FATHER'S EXAMPLE

A farmer returned home one evening and said to his boys, "I met Mr. B today and he wants to buy a cow. He's coming over in the morning to look at ours. I'd like to get rid of that good-for-nothing old thing we all hate so much to milk and who breaks down every fence on the place. I've been thinking that it would be a good plan to let her go tonight and tomorrow morning without milking and of course she'll have a big udder and will draw his attention. When he asks about her, you boys chip in and say, 'Dad, you surely aren't going to sell old Fill-pail, are you?' Then I'll say, 'Course not. We couldn't spare her. She's the best cow we got.' That will make him want the old hussy more than ever. Now you'll have to be cute about it and not say too much, but say enough. Just follow me, and you'll see how to do the thing right."

Mr. B came as was expected, and the prearranged plan worked out as if on ball bearings. Sundry sly winks were exchanged between the farmer and his sons; and behind the backs of their father and the visitor, as the money was changing hands, the boys could hardly restrain their mirth. It was not often that a snicker of such proportions came to the farm. When the purchaser leading "Fill-pail" was out of earshot, the father and the boys shouted with glee.

What became of the stranger and the cow? That isn't important, and I don't know. But I do know what became of the boys. They have both served terms in the penitentiary for cattle stealing. Who was to blame?

—Alonzo A. Hinckley

GENEALOGY AND INSPIRATION

When I went on my first mission to Holland, there were three of us who went to that land—a brother from Idaho, one from Spanish Fork, Utah, and myself. We landed in Rotterdam. One of them was sent up to the north. He had a German name and when he was called to go to Holland his people were disappointed, feeling that he ought to go to Germany where he could look up the genealogy of his father's people.

When he arrived in the northern part of Holland, what we call Groningen, he was sent out into the little city of Veendam, and he and his companion went looking for a place to live—furnished rooms.

This young man said to his companion, "This looks like a nice place; let's go in here."

After they were there a few weeks, he found that a record of his father's people had been brought across the border out of Germany, and his father's family never knew that their people had ever been in Holland.

Think of the inspiration of God that led the President of the Church to send that boy to Holland, and the inspiration that guided the president of the mission to send him up into the north, and the inspiration that guided the district president to send him to the little city of Veendam, about sixty thousand population at that time, and the same inspiration that led him and his companion to the very house where he found that record.

Now, he died over there with the smallpox. I was present at his burial. The city was going to burn the book because it had been handled by the deceased.

The district president said, "If you do, it will cost you five hundred dollars."

They said no book was worth that much, but they fumigated it page by page and sent it to the family. They did the temple work.

—*LeGrand Richards*

GO THAT WAY YOURSELF

There is practical wisdom in that comment of Josh Billings with regard to the precept "train up a child in the way he should go." He says, "It is a good plan to go that way two or three times yourself."

Parents often miss it by giving a pound of precept for every ounce of example. Too often the example set is quite the other way, and sharp-eared children are quick to perceive the discrepancy.

If a mother instructs her child carefully in the study of always speaking the truth, and then goes on to make a great fuss over some detested neighbor, telling her how delighted she is to see her, and begging her to stay and visit, depend upon it that there's a child there taking notes.

"Did you really like that painting, mother, or did you only say so?" asked the young lady of a friend of mine. It came out that mother "only said so," and it did not strengthen the faith of the listener in her mother's sincerity.

The father who would see his son grow up an honest, honorable man, must beware of any double-dealing, either with him or before his eyes. It does not strengthen a boy's faith in his father's integrity to have the calf that was given to him sold, and the proceeds put in his father's pocket. It angers him to have father sell the

berries he has worked hard to pick, and then invest the money in tobacco.

Go that way yourself, if you wish your child to walk in the straight way. Be patient, and discipline with love, remembering with humility how many times you also have stumbled before him.

THE HOME AS A MISSIONARY

I was over in Seoul in Korea recently, and one of the finest men we have over in that country is a man by the name of Dr. Ho Jik Kim. He is a graduate from Cornell University with a doctor's degree. He has returned to his native land now as an advisor to the Korean government. He is a leader of one of the educational institutions there, and around him he has gathered now thirty-four converts, many of them well-educated. We talked with him for some two hours, trying to lay a foundation that might establish itself into a beginning of missionary activities in the land of Korea. He told us about his conversion.

"The thing that attracted me to the Church," he explained, "was when I was invited into the home of two Latter-day Saint men who were on the faculty of Cornell University. The thing that I was most impressed by was the kind of home life they had. I never had been in homes where there was such a sweet relationship between husband and wife, and father and mother and children. I had seen them engage in family prayer. I was so impressed that I began to inquire about this religion of theirs. And one night after I had studied for a long time and had become convinced about the desirability of belonging to such a company, I knew first I must get a testimony. I went down on my knees and prayed nearly all night long and I received a testimony of the divinity of this work." But remember, it all started because of the excellent example of a family that lived the kind of home life that the gospel expects of true Latter-day Saints.

—*Harold B. Lee*

I MUST GO TO WILLIE

During the Civil War there was a woman in Maine who received a letter which read: "Willie is sick. He is dying." The mother read the letter and, looking up to her husband, said, "Father, I must go to Willie."

"No, wife, you cannot go," he replied. "You

know there is a line of bayonets between you and Willie."

She did what the Christian mother always does when her boy is in peril. She spread that letter before the Lord and prayed all night. Next morning she said, "Father, I must go to Willie. I must."

"Well, wife," he said, "I do not know what will come of this, but of course if you will go, there is the money."

She went down to Washington, and the man in the executive mansion, who had a very tender heart—Abraham Lincoln—brushed away a tear as he wrote, and handing her a paper, said, "Madam, that will take you to the enemy's line, but what will become of you after you get there, I cannot tell."

She took the paper and, coming down to the line, handed a guard the pass. He looked at it and at her, and said, "We don't take that thing here."

"I know it," she said, "but Willie, my boy is dying in Richmond, and I am going to him. Now shoot."

He did not shoot, but stood awed and hushed in the presence of a love that is more like God's than any other that surges in the human soul in its deathless unselfishness.

All that mother thought of was her boy. Smuggled through the lines, she went down to the hospital. The surgeon said to her, "Madam, you must be very careful. Your boy will survive no excitement."

She crept past cot after cot, and knelt at the foot of the one where her boy lay and, putting up her hands, prayed in smothered tones, "Oh God, spare my boy." The sick boy raised his white hands from under the sheet. The sound of his mother's voice had gone clear down into the valley and shadow of death, where the soul of the young man was going out in its ebbing tide. Raising his hand, he said, "Mother, I knew you would come." That boy grew to be a man, saved by a mother's love.

I'LL TAKE WHAT FATHER TAKES

"I'll take what father takes," was the remark that brought one parent to a realization of the wonderful influence he might exert in molding the life of his boy.

A boy had realized one of his fondest dreams; he had been taken down to spend a day in his father's office. Everything was fascinating. The newness and the reality of the situation simply lifted the boy out of his routine school life. And when at noon the father took him to the club for luncheon, his delight was complete.

And there is where the boy said to the waiter, "I'll take what father takes."

"Milk for two," the father said, changing his usual order for a beverage.

"I'll take what father takes." As the afternoon wore on, that father thought of the things which in his life he had taken which he would hate to have his boy indulge in. Cigars, cigarettes, a little gambling—all such regrettable indulgences were given a magnified significance.

That evening when father and son returned home, the boy glowed with enthusiasm as he related to his mother the events of the day.

"And to go," he said, "to the club and take just what father took!"

How the boy's delight struck home as a lesson to his father! It lingered with him—it made him say to his wife, "I'll so live from this day on that my boy can say, 'I'll take what father takes,' and I'll be able to be proud of him and he of me."

—*Adam S. Bennion*

LET MY DAD HOLD THE ROPE

A party of English botanists spent their vacation in the Swiss Alps collecting specimens of rare flowers. They started out one morning from a small village, and after several hours' climb came to a precipice overlooking a green valley dotted with a peculiar flower, which, examined through field glasses, proved to be of unusual value. From the cliff on which the party was standing to the valley was a sheer drop of several hundred feet. To descend would be impossible, and to reach the valley from another approach would mean a waste of several hours.

During the latter part of their climb, a small boy had attached himself to the party and had watched with interest the maneuvers of the botanists. After discussing the situation for several minutes, one of the party turned to the boy and said, "Young fellow, if you will let us tie a rope around your waist and lower you over this cliff so that you can dig up one of those plants for us, and let us pull you back up without harming the plant, we will give you five pounds."

The boy looked dazed for an instant, then ran off, apparently frightened at the prospect of being lowered over the cliff by a rope. But within a short time he returned, bringing with him an old man, bent and gray, with hands gnarled and calloused by hard labor. Upon reaching the party of botanists, the boy turned to the man who had made the offer and said:

"Sir, this is my dad. I'll go down in the valley if you'll let my dad hold the rope."

—David O. McKay

A LOVING COUPLE

I stood at my window only the other day and watched a couple going down the street—a big, strong young fellow and his wife, a beautiful woman, tagging behind him. I thought, "They are married, all right." If he had not been, why he would have hold of her arm, showing her a little attention and courtesy, and I felt like I would like to go out there and kick that fellow. She was good-looking, too. That made me dislike him more.

—Charles W. Nibley

MANY MOTHERS

Schumann's mother was gifted with music.

Gounod's mother was fond of painting and music.

Chopin's mother, like himself, was very delicate.

Milton's letters often allude to his mother in the most affectionate terms.

"All that I am, or ever hope to be, I owe to my angel mother," said Abraham Lincoln.

Raleigh said that he owed all his politeness of deportment to his mother.

Goethe pays several tributes in his writings to the character of his mother.

Haydn dedicated one of his most important instrumental compositions to his mother.

—Albert L. Zobell, Jr.
Discourse Cameos

MARRYING AN ANGEL

A young man described enthusiastically the qualities that *must* be possessed by his fortunate (?) future wife.

Said an old man who was listening, and looking over the young man pityingly, "You don't want no girl! You want an angel. And a pretty gol-darned-looking sight you'd be along-side of an angel."

MOTHER BEYMER'S DIVIDENDS

There died, recently, in a Western city, an old woman known as Mother Beymer. She was a thrifty, hardworking woman with just enough education to carry on a green grocery successfully.

She never had any children of her own, but in her long life had adopted, one after another, six-teen little orphans who otherwise would have died or had miserable or vicious lives.

She took some of them when they were babies, nursed, fed, clothed and worked for them precisely as if God had given them to herself. Very few of the townspeople, indeed, knew that they were not her own.

Some of the girls married. Others have trades. Two of her boys were killed at war. Three are thriving farmers. Two became ministers of the gospel. But, without an exception, all have led honest, useful lives.

Mother Beymer's shop was the largest in the town, and she worked early and late.

"You ought to be laying by money," a neighbor said to her once.

"My money's all invested," she said. "It's bringing in good dividends."

When she died, her children mourned for her with a gratitude which they would hardly have felt for a real mother.

Close beside the place where she was buried, a rich man who had "laid by" much money, was laid. But of all his wealth, only the ponderous marble monument remained which held him down.

But by the poor woman's grave stood the living men and women whom she had saved from ruin, and sent out into the world as its helpers and teachers. Money invested in this way will pay dividends forever.

MOTHER NEVER TOLD A LIE

A boy was discovered one morning lying in the grass in New Orleans. He was evidently bright and intelligent, but quite sick. A kind man went to him, shook him by the shoulder, and asked what he was doing there.

"Waiting for God to come for me."

"What do you mean?" asked the gentleman.

"God came for mother and father and took them away to His home up in the sky, and mother told me when she was sick that God would take care of me. I have no home and nobody to give me anything, so I came out here and have been looking for a long time up in the sky for God to come and take care of me, as mother said He would. He will come, won't He? Mother never told a lie."

"Yes, son," said the man, overcome with emotion. "He has sent me to take care of you."

The boy's eyes flashed with joy and he said, "Mother never told me a lie, sir, but you've taken a *long* time!"

A MOTHER'S JEWELS

In a far country, long ago, a very distinguished, though vain lady upon whom wealth had been lavished in the form of diamonds, rubies, emeralds, and pearls, exhibited her jewels before the thousands of people who came to see these brilliant necklaces, bracelets, and other adornments.

But in the crowd one woman was overheard to say, "Her jewels cannot compare with mine."

The vain woman, thinking that she herself had the most precious jewels in all the land, said to a servant, "Follow that woman. I must see her jewels."

The next morning the lady of wealth called upon the woman who had stood in the crowd. "Show me your jewels," she challenged.

Humbly the mother called to her side two little boys, and placing an arm around each of her sons, she faced the lady of wealth and influence and said, "These are my jewels."

—*David O. McKay*

MY MOTHER'S TRANSLATION

Four clergymen were discussing the merits of the various translations of the Bible. One liked the King James Version best because of its simple, beautiful English.

Another liked the American Revised Version best because it is more literal and comes nearer to the original Hebrew and Greek.

Still another liked Moffatt's translation because of its up-to-date vocabulary.

The fourth minister was silent. When asked to express his opinion, he replied, "I like my mother's translation best."

The other three expressed surprise. They did not know that his mother had translated the Bible. "Yes, she did," he replied. "She translated it into life, and it was the most convincing translation I ever saw."

—*Saints' Herald*

THE NICK OF TIME

A minister was asked to perform the wedding ceremony for a pair of happy lovers. They were both well-to-do, and had a large circle of fashionable friends who were invited to the ceremony. When the hour arrived, the church was packed with people, and all was ready. The groom and his companions were waiting, but for some reason the bride was not present. The minister, the groom, and the parents waited anxiously for her appearance. Finally she drove up with her bridesmaids and entered the church. When they had walked halfway up the aisle she was met by the groom, who then led her forward to the altar. Then the minister began the marriage ceremony, and asked the groom if he would have the woman for his wedded wife, and so forth, to which he answered, "I will." Then he turned to the bride and asked her, and she distinctly said, looking her intended husband in the face, "I will not."

This reply amazed and astonished all who heard it. She then said in a low voice to the minister that if he would dismiss the congregation and take her aside, she would explain why she had given such an answer.

The minister, seeing that she was sincere, complied with the request and told the groom to wait there. He brought her into a side room and she said to him, "I can't tell you how badly I feel. I had truly and devotedly loved my fiance. I had looked forward to a life of perfect happiness and joy. This morning, as you know, I was late in coming here, but it was not my fault. I arrived as soon as I could. When my future husband came to meet me in the aisle, instead of giving me looks of love and words of happiness, he swore at me, and said, 'If you expect to begin life by keeping me waiting for you, I'll teach you different after you're my wife.' The coarseness and cruelty of his words shocked me. I instantly made my decision. I made up my mind that it would be better to never be married than to have a union that would bring misery and grief. I know I could not be happy with such a man. And I have made up my mind not to marry him. Will you be so kind as to inform him of my determination and let me go?''

REPROVED BY A CHILD

A young missionary whose field of labor was in Hawaii tells a story about himself which illustrates how unexpected, startling and impressive a child's remark can be.

Years before his call to the mission field he had used tobacco, but previous to his mission he quit the habit, and for months did well in avoiding tobacco. Once, however, he became lonesome and dispirited and thought that he could find comfort in a cigarette. So he went out among the woods and rocks near the house of a native family where he was staying, rolled some tobacco in a paper and smoked it. He found temporary relief, and though conscience-smitten, repeated it several times on later occasions.

One day after he had smoked in the woods, he came into the house, sat down and busied himself with his thoughts. The only other occupants of the house were a five-year-old boy and his mother. This little child walked near where the young man sat, and, sniffing the air several times, ran to the door of the adjoining room and called out, "Mamma, mamma, the servant of God smokes!"

The mother, who was attending to her household duties, seemed not to hear the young boy, but the missionary was dumbfounded. And that was not the end of it, for the boy came back to convince himself that he smelled tobacco. Reassured, he ran to the door again and shouted, "Mamma, mamma, the servant of God smokes!"

The mother politely ignored the child's discovery, notwithstanding the fact that the little fellow insisted a third time on following up his investigations. The missionary was so overwhelmed with shame and confusion that, as he afterwards said in relating the incident, he would have preferred the earth to open and swallow him up than to stand accused and condemned by an innocent child. "If an angel had rebuked me," he said, "I could scarcely have been more deeply and lastingly impressed."

SHOW YOUR LOVE NOW

One long, hot day I met my father on the road to town. "I wish you would take this package to the village for me, Jim," he said, hesitatingly.

Now, I was a boy of twelve, not fond of work, and just out of the hayfield where I had been at work since daybreak. I was tired, dusty and hungry. It was two miles into town. I wanted to get my supper and to dress for my singing class.

My first impulse was to refuse, and to do it harshly. I was angry that he'd ask me after my long day's work. If I did refuse, he would go himself. He was a gentle, patient old man. But something stopped me.

"Of course I'll take it, father," I said heartily.

He gave me the package. "Thank you, Jim," he said. "I was going myself, but somehow I don't feel very strong today."

He walked with me to the road that turned off to the town, and as he left he put his hand on my arm, saying again, "Thank you, my son. You've always been a good boy to me."

I hurried into town and back again. When I came near the house, I saw a crowd of farm hands at the door. One of them came to me with tears rolling down his face.

"Your father!" he said. "He fell dead just as he reached the house. The last words he spoke were to you."

I am an old man now, but I have thanked God over and over again, in all these years that have passed since that hour, that those last words were, "You've always been a good boy to me."

SLOW CHILDREN

Napoleon Bonaparte and Arthur Wellesley, the Duke of Wellington, were both famous soldiers, and among the greatest military chieftains the world has known. Both were slow learners, not distinguishing themselves in any way in school. Wellesley's mother considered him to be a dunce and "food for powder."

General Thomas Jonathan Jackson, popularly known as "Stonewall Jackson," was noted as a boy and as a student at West Point Military Academy for his slowness. Ulysses S. Grant, commander-in-chief of the northern forces in the Civil War and later President of the United States, was called "Useless Grant" by his mother.

Sir Walter Scott was regarded as a numbskull, and after his studies at Edinburgh University, one of his professors stated, "Dunce he is and dunce he will remain."

Benjamin Disraeli, the late prime minister of England, made a fool of himself at his first speech before the House of Commons. The speech was a failure. Every sentence was greeted with loud laughter. But was he discouraged? No. He told them, "Gentlemen, I have begun several things many times, and have succeeded in them at last. I will sit down now, but the time will come when you will hear me." That time came.

A SYSTEM IN TWO WORDS

"What is needed," asked Napoleon one day to an aide, "in order for the youth of France to be well educated?"

"Good mothers," was the reply.

Napoleon, struck with this answer, said, "Here is a system in two words."

—*J. S. C. Abbott*

A BOY'S MOTHER

My mother she's so good to me,
Ef I was good as I could be,
I couldn't be as good—no, sir.—
Can't any boy be good as her.

She loves me when I'm glad er sad;
She loves me when I'm good er bad;
An', what's a funniest thing, she says
She loves me when she punishes.

I don't like her to punish me,—
That don't hurt—but it hurts to see
Her cryin'.—Nen I cry; an' nen
We both cry an' be good again.

She loves me when she cuts an' sews
My little cloak an' Sund'y clothes;
An' when my Pa comes home to tea,
She loves him most as much as me.

She laughs an' tells him all I said,
An' grabs me up an' pats my head;
An' I hug her, an' hug my Pa,
An' love him put' nigh as much as Ma.

—*James Whitcomb Riley*

THE GIFT

God thought to give the sweetest thing
In His almighty power
To earth; and deeply pondering
What it should be—one hour
In fondest joy and love of heart
Outweighing every other,
He moved the gates of heaven apart
And gave to earth—a Mother!

—*Author Unknown*

HOUSE AND HOME

A house is built of logs and stone,
Of tiles and posts and piers;
A home is built of loving deeds
That stand a thousand years.

—*Victor Hugo*

A MOTHER'S NAME

No painter's brush nor poet's pen,
In justice to her fame;
Has ever reached half high enough
To write a mother's name.

—*Author Unknown*

Godhead

AN ATHEIST'S BOAST

A professed atheist was once at a party given by a lady. He talked vigorously of his disbelief in God. When no one agreed with him, he exclaimed impatiently, "I could not have guessed that in a company of intellectual beings, I alone could have been found without belief in God."

"Excuse me, sir," said the lady, "you are not alone. My cat and dog lying over there share your ignorance. Only they aren't foolish enough to boast about it."

—S. B. Gould

THE BEST REFUGE

A school class was discussing where their refuge would be if their country were invaded. Each child in his turn told of his favorite hiding place. When each had had his say, one child asked the teacher where she would hide.

"My refuge," the teacher replied, "would be in God."

BETTER THAN CLOCKWORK

A minister asked an old man his reasons for believing in the existence of God. "Sir," he said, "I have been here for fifty years. Every day since I have been in this world I see the sun rise in the east and set in the west. The North Star stands where it did the first time I saw it; the Big and Little Dippers keep on the same path in the sky, and never go astray. It isn't so with man's work. He makes clocks and watches; they may run well for awhile, but they fall apart and stop. But the sun and moon and stars keep on going the same way the whole time."

CHRISTMAS GIFTS

I didn't question Timmy, age nine, or his seven-year-old brother Billy about the brown wrapping paper they passed back and forth between them as we visited each store.

Every year at Christmastime, our service club takes the children from poor families in our town on a personally conducted shopping tour. I was assigned Timmy and Billy, whose father was out of work. After giving them the allotted $4.00 each, we began our trip. At different stores I made suggestions, but always their answer was a solemn shake of the head, no. Finally I asked, "Where would you suggest we look?"

"Could we go to a shoe store, sir?" answered Timmy. "We'd like a pair of shoes for our daddy so he can go to work."

In the shoe store the clerk asked what the boys wanted. Out came the brown paper. "We want a pair of work shoes to fit this foot," they said. Billy explained that it was a pattern of their daddy's foot. They had drawn it while he was asleep in a chair.

The clerk held the paper against a measuring stick, then walked away. Soon, he came with an open box. "Will these do?" he asked. Timmy and Billy handled the shoes with great eagerness. "How much do they cost?" asked Billy. Then Timmy saw the price on the box. "They're $16.95," he said in dismay. "We only have $8.00."

I looked at the clerk and he cleared his throat. "That's the regular price," he said, "but they're on sale; $3.98, today only." Then, with shoes happily in hand the boys bought gifts for their mother and two little sisters. Not once did they think of themselves.

The day after Christmas the boys' father stopped me on the street. The new shoes were on his feet, gratitude was in his eyes. "I just thank Jesus for people who care," he said. "And I thank Jesus for your two sons," I replied. "They really taught me more about Christmas in one evening than I had learned in a lifetime."

—Jack Smith

THE FOOTPRINTS OF GOD

"How do you know," a nomad was asked, "that there is a God?"

"In the same way," he replied, "that I know, on looking at the sand, when a man or an animal has crossed the desert—by His footprints in the world around me."

—*Canon Liddon*

A FORGIVING GOD

An old man and his wife were annoyed by their neighbor's cattle going over their fences into their wheat and grass, and causing great loss to the poor old people. David, the old man, at last got impatient, and one day, entering the house, said to his wife, "Our neighbor's cattle have been in our wheat again. I'll make him pay the damage this time."

"Don't talk about paying, David. 'I will repay,' saith the Lord."

"No, indeed, He won't," said David. "He's too ready to forgive to do that."

GOD, THE CENTER

For more than fifty centuries men watched the starlit sky, noted the changes of the planets, and endeavored to discover the laws which governed their movements; they took careful observations, made elaborate calculations, and yet the law of the harmony of the heavens remained a mystery. The stars were still supposed to follow fantastic circles which no rule of science could explain; their orbits formed a labyrinth of which the most learned failed to find the clue. One day a man said, "The sun, and not the earth, is the center from which the worlds must be regarded." At once the harmony appeared; planets and their satellites moved in regular orbits; the system of the universe was revealed. God is the sun and the true center of the spiritual world; only in the light in which He dwells can the destinies of man be truly read.

—*Eugene Bersier*

GOD WILL KNOW YOU

One evening a man was strolling along a street to pass the time. His attention was attracted by the remark of a little girl to a companion in front of a fruit store: "I wish I had an orange for ma." The gentleman saw that the children, though poorly dressed, were clean and neat, and calling them into the store, he loaded them with fruit and candies.

"What's your name?" asked one of the girls.

"Why do you want to know?" asked the gentleman.

"I want to pray for you," was the reply.

The gentleman turned to leave, scarcely daring to speak, when the little one added, "Well, it don't matter, I suppose. God will know you anyhow."

HE KNOWS WHAT'S BEST

An aged hermit planted an olive tree near his cave; and then, thinking it might want water, he prayed to God to send rain. So the rain came down and watered his olive tree. Then he thought a little warm sun would do it good; so he prayed for warmth and sunshine, and the sun shone, and it was very hot. Then, as the sapling looked somewhat feeble, the hermit thought, "What it now wants is a little frost to brace it." Accordingly he prayed for frost, and that night the frost covered the ground. But the olive somehow did not seem to thrive, so he thought that possibly a warm southerly wind might help it on; and he prayed that the south wind might blow upon his tree. The hot south wind blew, and the olive died!

Some days after, he was visiting a brother hermit, and he noticed that he had a remarkably fine olive tree. "Why, brother," he said, "how do you manage to get your olive tree to thrive so well?"

"I don't know that I did anything specially to it, but I just planted it, and God blessed it, and it grew."

"Ah, brother, I planted an olive tree, and when I thought it wanted water I prayed God to give it rain, and He sent rain; and when I thought it wanted sun I prayed for it, and the sun shone; and when I thought it wanted bracing I prayed for frost, and the frost came. God sent me everything that I prayed for, but my tree died!"

"And I," replied the other, "just simply prayed that God would take care of my tree, and then left it in His hands to arrange the how and the when, because I felt sure He knew what was best for my tree better than I did!"

IN GOD'S HANDS

When Bulstrode Whitelocke was embarking, in the year 1653, as ambassador for Sweden, he was disturbed as he reflected on the state of the nation. A good and confidential servant slept in an adjacent bed, who, finding that his master could not sleep, at length said, "Sir, can I ask you a question?"

"Certainly."

"Sir, don't you think that God governed the world very well before you came into it?"

"Undoubtedly."

"And pray, sir, don't you think He will govern it quite as well when you are gone out of it?"

"Certainly."

"Then, sir, don't you think you may trust Him to govern it properly as long as you live?"

To this last question Whitelocke had nothing to reply, but, turning himself about, soon fell fast alseep.

LOVING GOD

A mother had been talking to her little girl about loving God. The child replied, "Mother, I have never seen God. How can I love Him?"

A few days later the mother received a package from a friend, and in the package was a beautiful picture book for the little girl. The child took the book and was for some time occupied in looking at the pictures; but soon she exclaimed, "Oh mother, I love the lady that sent me this book!"

"But you've never seen her, my dear," said the mother.

"No," answered the child, "but I love her because she sent me this beautiful present."

SINGING TO THE LORD

We used to have here a number of years ago a young man who came from Wales. He did not have the opportunity of a college education, but he was a Welshman, full of Welsh music. When he came here, he became the leader of this great (Tabernacle) choir. He it was who had joy, along with those who preceded him and those who followed, in building a choir not just to sing, but to sing praises to our Heavenly Father.

I want to tell you a little incident about this man, Evan Stephens. Some very prominent people were coming here. In that day we did not have so many visitors of prominence. We were too far out in the wilderness. One of our good bishops came to Evan Stephens and said: "Brother Stephens, I have some company coming next Sunday to the religious meeting"—(we used to have a meeting here at two o'clock every Sunday)—"and I hope you are going to have some good music."

Brother Stephens said: "All right, Bishop, we will have good music."

The bishop did not think that was enough assurance, so he pressed it a little. He said: "These people are not ordinary people. They are men of affairs and wealth. Their families are wealthy, and I would like them to see just what a fine choir we have. Now, won't you give us something just a little extra?"

Brother Stephens said: "Bishop, we have already had our rehearsal. The music has all been prepared. I don't see how we can make a change. I think it will be good enough for your friends."

The bishop pressed him a little harder, and then Brother Stephens got riled and said: "Now, look here, Bishop, we have prepared the music for next Sunday to sing to the Lord, and I think if it is good enough for the Lord, it is good enough for your company."

—*George Albert Smith*

SOMEONE TO HOLD ONTO

A man, his wife and two-year-old daughter were traveling by train from Stockholm to southern Sweden. The little girl was anxious to sit on the table and look out through the compartment window.

All at once the train gave a jerk and the little girl nearly fell to the floor. Her father took hold of her, but she did not like this. She wanted to take care of herself. The mother suggested that he hold the child's dress without her knowing it. This worked splendidly.

Suddenly the train rushed into a tunnel. The father felt two small arms around his neck; a little cheek softly touched his own. Father was near; the child felt safe.

Like this child, we wish to go our own way in life. We put away all authority—we think! This goes for a time, but soon we meet the tunnels of life. Especially in those moments it is a blessing for us to know that our Heavenly Father is near to assure and help us.

—*Victor Brattstrom*

SPEAKING WITH THE SPIRIT

When I was made the president of the Tooele Stake of Zion and made my maiden speech, I ran out of ideas in seven and a half minutes by the watch. That night I heard a very contemptuous voice in the dark. "Well, it is a pity if the General Authorities of the Church had to import a boy from the city to come out here to preside over us, they could not have found one with sense enough to talk ten minutes." So you see he held his stopwatch on me; he knew I did not take ten minutes. I knew I did not, because I timed myself—seven and a half minutes was the limit. The next speech, and the next, and the next were the same. One of them was only five minutes. The next speech was at a little town called Vernon, sometimes called Stringtown, as it spread over twelve miles as I remember it.

As we were going to the meeting I was with the bishop, Brother John C. Sharp, and I did not see anybody going to meeting. The bishop said, "Oh, there will be somebody there." We were going up a little hill and when we got to the top of the hill we found a number of wagons and white tops at the meetinghouse—it was a long meetinghouse—but did not see anybody going in.

I said, "There doesn't seem to be anybody going to meeting."

He replied, "Oh, I think you'll find somebody there."

When we got inside, the meetinghouse was crowded. We went in at two minutes to two and nobody else came in afterwards. I congratulated the bishop after the meeting on having educated his people to be so prompt.

"Most of them have to hitch up a team to come here," he said, "and I have told them they could just as well hitch it up a few minutes earlier and be there at two minutes to two o'clock, so there will be no disturbance."

I had taken a couple of brethren with me that day to do the preaching. I got up expecting to take five or six minutes and talked forty-five minutes with as much ease, if not more, than I have ever enjoyed since. I shed tears of gratitude that night to the Lord for the inspiration of his Spirit.

The next Sunday I went to Grantsville, the largest town in Tooele County, and got up with all the assurance in the world and told the Lord I would like to talk forty-five minutes, and ran out of ideas in five. I not only ran out of ideas in five

minutes, but I was perspiring and walked fully two and a half, if not three miles, after that meeting, to the farthest haystack in Grantsville, and kneeled behind that haystack and asked the Lord to forgive me for my egotism in that meeting and made a pledge to the Lord that never again in my life would I stand before an audience without asking for His Spirit to help me, nor would I take personally the credit for anything I said, and I have kept this pledge.

—*Heber J. Grant*

TAKE CARE WHAT YOU SAY

Latimer, while preaching one day before Henry VIII, stood up in the pulpit and, seeing the king, said to himself, "Latimer, Latimer, Latimer, take care what you say, for the great King Henry VIII is here." Then he paused, and said, "Latimer, Latimer, Latimer, take care what you say, for the great King of kings is here."

THOU ART MINE

The sun does not shine for a few trees and flowers, but for the whole world's joy. The lonely pine on the mountaintop waves its boughs and cries, "Thou art my sun." And the little violet lifts its blue cup, and whispers, "Thou art my sun." And the grain in a thousand fields rustles in the wind and says, "Thou art my sun." So God sits in heaven, not for a favored few, but for the universe of life; and there is no creature so poor or so low that he may not look up with childlike confidence and say, "My Father, Thou art mine."

—*Henry Ward Beecher*

WHEN I THINK OF GOD

When the poet Carpani asked his friend, Haydn, how it happened that his church music was always so cheerful, the great composer made a most beautiful reply: "I cannot," he said, "make it otherwise. I write according to the thoughts I feel; when I think upon God my heart is so full of joy that the notes dance and leap, as it were, from my pen; and since God has given me a cheerful heart, I'm sure I'll be forgiven for serving Him with a cheerful spirit."

WHERE AND WHERE NOT IS GOD?

A child was asked, "If you can tell me where God is, I'll give you an orange."

The child replied, "If you can tell me where he is not, I'll give you two."

WHO WILL BE THERE?

"I don't know whether to show up at stake conference or not," said a member to his stake president. "Will there be a General Authority there?"

"The Lord will be there," said the stake president, "and that's about the highest authority I can think of."

ATHEIST

For you I paint the scarab's horny back,
Blending sheen of copper, green and tawny gold;
For your wonderment I joint the tiny insect's leg,
I pack his body with resilient nerves;
He knows his path,
His short life is complete.
Not the endless spaces overhead,
Not the true high-swung stars
Need a mightier hand than this despised atom.
Daily you crunch a thousand miracles
Beneath your careless foot....
And yet you say:
There is no God.

—*Florence E. Milcke*

CHRIST IS CRUCIFIED ANEW

Not only once, and long ago,
There on Golgotha's rugged side,
Has Christ, the Lord, been crucified
Because He loved a lost world so.
But hourly souls, sin-satisfied,
Mock His great love, flout His commands.
And I drive nails deep in His hands,
You thrust the spear within His side.

—*John Richard Moreland*

A CHRISTMAS CAROL

The Christ-child lay on Mary's lap,
His hair was like a light.
(O weary, weary were the world,
But here is all alright.)

The Christ-child lay on Mary's breast,
His hair was like a star.
(O stern and cunning are the kings,
But here the true hearts are.)

The Christ-child lay on Mary's heart,
His hair was like a fire.
(O weary, weary is the world,
But here the world's desire.)

The Christ-child stood at Mary's knee.
His hair was like a crown,
And all the flowers looked up at Him,
And all the stars looked down.

—*G. K. Chesterton*

A CHRISTMAS CAROL

"What means this glory round our feet,"
The Magi mused, "more bright than morn?"
And voices chanted clear and sweet,
"Today the Prince of Peace is born!"

"What means that star," the Shepherds said,
"That brightens through the rocky glen?"
And angels, answering overhead,
Sang, "Peace on earth, good-will to men!"

'Tis eighteen hundred years and more
Since those sweet oracles were dumb;
We wait for Him, like them of yore;
Alas, He seems so slow to come!

But it was said, in words of gold
Not time or sorrow e'er shall dim,
That little children might be bold
In perfect trust to come to Him.

All round about our feet shall shine
A light like that the wise men saw,
If we our loving wills incline
To that sweet Life which is the Law.

So shall we learn to understand
The simple faith of shepherds then,

And, clasping kindly hand in hand,
Sing, "Peace on earth, good-will to men!"

And they who do their souls no wrong,
But keep at eve the faith of morn,
Shall daily hear the angel-song,
"Today the Prince of Peace is born!"
                              —*James Russell Lowell*

CHRISTMAS EVERYWHERE

Everywhere, everywhere, Christmas tonight!
Christmas in lands of the fir-tree and pine,
Christmas in lands of the palm-tree and vine,
Christmas where snow peaks stand solemn and
    white,
Christmas where cornfields stand sunny and
    bright.
Christmas where children are hopeful and gay,
Christmas where old men are patient and gray,
Christmas where peace, like a dove in his flight,
Broods o'er brave men in the thick of the fight;
Everywhere, everywhere, Christmas tonight!

For the Christ-child who comes is the Master
    of all;
No palace too great, no cottage too small.
                              —*Phillips Brooks*

THE COMPANION

Here in my workshop where I toil
Till head and hands are well-nigh spent;
Out on the road where the dust and soil
Fall thick on garments worn and rent;
Or in the kitchen where I bake
The bread the little children eat—
He comes, His hand of strength I take,
And every lonely task grows sweet.
                              —*Author Unknown*

DELIGHT IN GOD ONLY

In having all things, and not Thee, what have I?
Not having Thee, what have my labours got?
Let me enjoy but Thee, what further crave I?
And having Thee alone, what have I not?
I wish nor sea nor land; nor would I be
Possessed of heaven, heaven unpossessed of
    Thee.
                              —*Francis Quarles*

EVENTIDE

At cool of day, with God I walk
My garden's grateful shade;
I hear His voice among the trees,
And I am not afraid.
He speaks to me in every wind,
He smiles from every star;
He is not deaf to me, nor blind,
Nor absent, nor afar.

His hand that shuts the flowers to sleep,
Each in its dewy fold,
Is strong my feeble life to keep,
And competent to hold.

The powers below and powers above,
Are subject to His care—
I cannot wander from His love
Who loves me everywhere.

Thus dowered, and guarded thus, with Him
I walk this peaceful shade;
I hear His voice among the trees,
And I am not afraid.
                              —*Caroline Atherton Mason*

GOD OF THE EARTH, THE SKY, THE SEA

God of the earth, the sky, the sea,
Maker of all above, below,
Creation lives and moves in Thee;
Thy present life through all doth flow.

Thy love is in the sun-shine's glow,
Thy life is in the quickening air;
When lightnings flash and storm winds blow,
There is Thy power, Thy law is there.

We feel Thy calm at evening's hour,
Thy grandeur in the march of night,
And when the morning breaks in power,
We hear Thy word, "Let there be light."

But higher far, and far more clear,
Thee in man's spirit we behold,
Thine image and Thyself are there,—
The in-dwelling God, proclaimed of old.
                              —*Samuel Longfellow*

IMMANENCE

Could my heart but see Creation as God sees it,—
    from within;
See His grace behind its beauty, see His will
    behind its force;
See the flame of life shoot upward when the
    April days begin;
See the wave of life rush outward from its pure
    eternal source;

Could I see the summer sunrise glow with God's
    transcendent hope;
See His peace upon the waters in the moonlight
    summer night;
See Him nearer still when, blinded, in the depths
    of gloom I grope,—
See the darkness flash and quiver with the
    gladness of His light;

Could I see the red-hot passion of His love
    resistless burn
Through the dumb despair of winter, through the
    frozen lifeless clod;—
Could I see what lies around me as God sees it,
    I should learn
That its outward life is nothing, that its inward
    life is God.

—*Edmond G. A. Holmes*

_____

INDIFFERENCE

When Jesus came to Golgotha they hanged Him
    on a tree,
They drove great nails through hands and feet,
    and made a Calvary;
They crowned Him with a crown of thorns,
    red were His wounds and deep,
For those were crude and cruel days, and
    human flesh was cheap.

When Jesus came to Birmingham they simply
    passed Him by,
They never hurt a hair of Him, they only
    let Him die;
For men had grown more tender, and they would
    not give Him pain,
They only just passed down the street,
    and left Him in the rain.

Still Jesus cried, "Forgive them, for they know
    not what they do,"

And still it rained the wintry rain that
    drenched Him through and through;
The crowds went home and left the streets
    without a soul to see,
And Jesus crouched against a wall and cried
    for Calvary.

—*G. A. Studdert-Kennedy*

_____

IT WAS NOT STRANGE

He came to be The Light,
And so it was not strange
A blazing star should pencil out his path
As Heaven unfurled its glory
On the night!

Wise kings came from afar!
Could aught more fitting be
Than kneeling sovereigns to greet
The King of kings—sweet Baby
Of their star?

With staffs, and sandal-shod
The shepherds came to search;
Such gentle men—it was not strange that they
Should find in Bethlehem
The Lamb of God!

—*Esther Lloyd Hagg*

_____

NO SWEETER THING

Life holds no sweeter thing than this—to teach
A little child the tale most loved on earth
And watch the wonder deepen in his eyes
The while you tell him of the Christ Child's birth;

The while you tell of shepherds and a song,
Of gentle, drowsy beasts and fragrant hay
On which that starlit night in Bethlehem
God's tiny Son and His young mother lay.

Life holds no sweeter thing than this—to tell
A little child, while Christmas candles glow,
The story of a Babe whose humble birth
Became the loveliest of truths we know.

—*Adelaide Love*

_____

ONE WORLD

I raised my eyes aloft, and I beheld
The scattered chapters of the Universe

Gathered and bound into a single book
By the austere and tender hand of God.
                                    —*Dante Alighieri*
                          From *The Divine Comedy*

———————

SINCE GOD IS THERE

My Lord, how full of sweet content,
I pass my years of banishment!
Wherever I dwell, I dwell with thee,
In Heaven, in earth, or on the sea.

To me remains nor place nor time;
My country is in every clime:
I can be calm and free from care
On any shore, since God is there.
                                    —*Madame Guyon*

———————

THE SONG OF THE CHILDREN

The world is ours till sunset,
Holly and fire and snow;
And the name of our dead brother
Who loved us long ago.

The grown folk mighty and cunning,
They write His name in gold;
But we can tell a little
Of the million tales He told.

He taught them laws and watchwords,
To preach and struggle and pray;
But He taught us deep in the hayfield
The games that the angels play.

Had He stayed here for ever,
Their world would be wise as ours—
And the king be cutting capers,
And the priest be picking flowers.

But the dark day came: they gathered:
On their faces we could see
They had taken and slain our brother,
And hanged Him on a tree.
                                    —*G. K. Chesterton*

———————

THESE ARE THY GLORIOUS WORKS

These are thy glorious works, Parent of good,
Almighty! Thine this universal frame,
Thus wondrous fair! Thyself how wonderous
      then!
Unspeakable! who sitt'st above these Heavens
To us invisible, or dimly seen
In these Thy lowest works; yet these declare
Thy goodness beyond thought and power divine.
                                    —*John Milton*
                          From *Paradise Lost*, Book V

———————

THY PRESENCE

Thou layest Thy hand on the fluttering heart
And sayest, "Be still!"
The shadow and silence are only a part
Of Thy sweet will.
Thy Presence is with me, and where Thou art
I feel no ill.
                                    —*Frances Ridley Havergal*

———————

TRUE RICHES

Of all the prizes
That earth can give,
This is the best:
To find Thee, Lord,
A living Presence near
And in Thee rest!

Friends, fortune, fame,
Or what might come to me—
I count all loss
If I find not
Companionship
With Thee!
                                    —*Author Unknown*

———————

Honesty and Courage

ANDREW MARVELL AND THE BRIBE

Andrew Marvell, a famous poet, was chosen as a member of the British Parliament in the reign of Charles II. He was a man of integrity, and such persons seem to have been rare in that reign. The government wished to bring him over to their side, and believing that a man as poor as Marvell could easily be bought, sent the treasurer, who had been a friend of his at school, to see him. The friend, on leaving, slipped into Marvell's hand a check for a thousand pounds, and then went to his carriage. Marvell called the treasurer back, and then summoned Jack, his servant-boy.

"Jack, what did I have for dinner yesterday?"

"Don't you know, sir? The little shoulder of mutton you ordered me to bring you from the market."

"Quite right, child. And what do I have for today?"

"Don't you know, sir, that you asked me to put the bones aside to make soup?"

"That's right, child." Then, turning to the astonished treasurer, he said, "Do you hear that? Andrew Marvell's dinner is provided. There is your piece of paper. I don't want it. The ministry must seek other men for their purpose."

BY LAND OR BY SEA

Two saints were being persecuted by a town rogue who threatened to tie them up and throw them in the river.

"Sir," said one of the saints, "we are going to heaven, and it matters very little to us whether we go there by land or by water."

DISCHARGED FOR HONESTY

A father helped get his son an apprenticeship with a merchant in a large city. For awhile all went well. But one day the son sold a dress to a lady, and as he was folding it up, he saw a flaw in the silk, and remarked, "Ma'am, I must point out a problem with this dress." The lady decided not to purchase the dress after all.

The merchant, however, had overheard the boy's remark and was furious. He immediately wrote the father and told him to come get his son, for, he said, "he will never make a merchant."

The father, who had brought up his son with the strictest care, was quite surprised and grieved, and hurried to the city to see where his son had gone wrong. When he reached the city he asked the merchant, "Why won't my son make a good merchant?"

"Because he has bad business sense. A couple of days ago he voluntarily told a lady who was buying a dress that there was a flaw in it and I lost a sale. Buyers need to watch out for themselves. If they can't find flaws it's foolish for me to point them out."

"And is this the problem?" asked the father.

"Yes," said the merchant. "Otherwise your son does quite well."

"Then I love my son better than ever," said the father, "and I thank you for telling me of the matter. I would not for the world have him in your store another day. Good-bye."

THE EARL AND THE FARMER

A farmer called on the Earl Fitzwilliam of England, claiming that his crop of wheat had been seriously injured in a field next to a certain forest where the earl frequently went to hunt. He said that the young wheat had been so cut up and destroyed by the horses of the earl and his party that, in some parts, he had no hopes of it growing.

"Well, my friend," said the earl, "I'm sure that we have frequently met in that field, and that we have done considerable injury, and if you can get an estimate of the loss you have sustained I'll repay you."

The farmer replied that, anticipating the earl's consideration and kindness, he had asked a friend to help him estimate the damage, and they thought that fifty pounds would cover the value of the lost wheat. The earl immediately gave him the money.

As the harvest approached, however, it was obvious that in that area where the horses had trampled the earth the wheat was the strongest and richest. The farmer went again to the earl.

"I've come concerning my field of wheat next to the forest," said the farmer.

"Well, my friend, didn't I pay you enough to cover the loss?"

"Yes, sir. I find that I have sustained no loss at all, for the wheat is best where the horses cut up the land. I'm therefore returning your fifty pounds."

"Ah," said the earl, "this is what I like. This is as it should be between men." He then asked the farmer about his family, how many children he had, a little bit about each, and so forth. The earl then went into another room, and returning, presented the farmer with a check for one hundred pounds, saying, "Take care of this, and when your oldest son is of age, give it to him, and tell him the occasion that produced it."

A GOOD WITNESS

A boy twelve years old was the important witness in a lawsuit. One of the lawyers, after questioning him severely, said, "Your father has been talking to you and telling you how to testify, hasn't he?"

"Yes," said the boy.

"Now," said the lawyer, "just tell us how your father told you to testify."

"Well," said the boy modestly, "Father told me the lawyers would try and tangle me in my testimony, and if I would just be careful and tell the truth, I could tell the same thing every time."

HE'S STILL ALIVE TO ME

A man once bought a pair of shoes from a cobbler, for which he promised to pay him soon. Several days later the man returned to the cobbler's shop with the money, but found that the cobbler in the meantime had died. The man was secretely elated, thinking he could now keep the money and the shoes. His conscience, however, wouldn't allow him to rest. He returned to the cobbler's shop and, casting the money inside, said, "Go your way. He may be dead to the rest of the world, but he's still alive to me."

AN HONEST BOY

A young boy was going away to boarding school, and his mother sewed a hundred dollars in his jacket, saying as she did so, "Now make me a promise that, whatever happens, you will never tell a lie." The boy promised and set out on his journey.

Late that night in a big city bus station, while waiting for his transfer, he was accosted by a group of thieves. They seized him and one said, "Do you have any money?"

The boy answered, "Yes, I have a hundred dollars sewn inside my jacket."

The thief laughed and let him go, thinking that he was only joking.

One of the other thieves grabbed him again, and asked, "Are you sure you don't have any money?"

The boy answered, "I already told you. I have one hundred dollars sewn inside my jacket."

The leader of the group, tired of playing around, got angry and told the boy if he had any money, he'd better tell them where it was.

The boy said, "I have one hundred dollars sewn inside my jacket."

The leader motioned to one of the other men and told him to rip the jacket open. They were all surprised when they did find money where the boy had told them.

"Why did you tell us this?" asked the leader.

"Because before I left I promised my mother I would never tell a lie."

The thief was so struck by the child's honesty that he ordered the money put back in the jacket and told him to hurry or he'd miss the bus.

AN HONEST CONFESSION

In the early part of the reign of Louis XVI, a German prince, traveling through France, visited the arsenal at Toulon where the galley slaves were kept. The commandant, in respect for the prince's rank, said he was welcome to set free any one galley slave.

The prince, wanting to make the best use of this privilege, spoke to many of the slaves, asking why they were condemned to the galleys. Injustice, oppression, false accusations were claimed by one after another as the causes of their being there. In fact, they were all injured and ill-treated persons. At last he came to one who, when asked the same question, answered, "Your Highness, I have no reason to complain—I have been a very wicked, desperate wretch. I have deserved to be broken alive on the wheel. I find it a great mercy that I am here."

The prince fixed his eyes upon him, and said, "You wicked wretch! It is a pity you should be placed among so many honest men. By your own confession, you are bad enough to corrupt them all; but you shall not stay with them another day."

Then, turning to the officer, he said, "This is the man, sir, whom I wish to be released."

HONEST TIMES

At one time in the Highlands of Scotland, asking for a receipt or promissory note was considered an insult, and such a thing as a breach of contract was rarely heard of, so strictly did the people regard their honor. A farmer from that area had been to the lowlands and had there acquired worldly wisdom.

After returning to his native place he needed some money, and requested a loan from a gentleman in the neighborhood. The latter, Mr. Stewart, complied and counted out the gold, when the farmer immediately wrote out a receipt.

"And what is this, man?" cried Mr. Stewart, on receiving the slip of paper.

"That is a receipt, sir, binding me to give you back your gold at the right time."

"Binding you, indeed! Well, my man, if you can't trust yourself I'm sure I'll not trust you! Such as you can't have my gold," and gathering it up he returned it to his desk and locked it up.

"But, sir, I might die," replied the needy Scot, unwilling to surrender his hope of the loan; "and perhaps my sons might refuse to pay you, but the bit of paper would compel them."

"Compel them to sustain their dead father's honor!" cried the enraged Celt. "They'll need compelling to do right, if this is the road you're leading them. You can go elsewhere for money, I tell you, but you'll find none about here that'll put more faith in a bit of paper than a neighbor's word of honor and his love of right."

AN INDICATION OF CHARACTER

Some years ago there lived in New York a shrewd old merchant named Aymar. He used to receive cargos of mahogany and logwood, which were sold at auction.

On one occasion a cargo was to be sold at Jersey City, and all hands started from the auctioneer's store to cross the ferry. When they were going through the gate, Mr. Aymar noticed one of the largest buyers slip through the gate without paying the fare. He told the auctioneer not to take a bid from that man.

"Why," said the auctioneer, with an expression of surprise, "I thought he was good!"

"So did I," answered Mr. Aymar, "but I have changed my mind, and I will not trust him a dollar."

A few months proved the accuracy of the judgment of Mr. Aymar, for the slippery merchant went bankrupt and did not pay five cents on the dollar.

LAW AND HONESTY

After listening carefully to the statement of his case by a client, Abraham Lincoln said: "Yes, there is no reasonable doubt but that I can gain your case for you. I can set a whole neighborhood at loggerheads! I can distress a widowed mother and her six fatherless children, and thereby get for you six hundred dollars which rightfully belongs, it appears to me, as much to the woman and her children as it does to you. You must remember that some things that are legally right are not morally right. I shall not take your case, but will give you a little advice, for which I charge you nothing. You seem to be a sprightly, energetic man. I would advise you to try your hand at making six hundred dollars some other way."

THE LIE STICKS

A Sunday School teacher asked one of her students, "Would you tell a lie for three cents?"

"No, ma'am," answered the boy very decidedly.

"For ten cents?"

"No, ma'am."

"For a dollar?"

"No, ma'am."

"For a thousand dollars?"

The boy was staggered. A thousand dollars looked big. It would buy a lot of things. While he was thinking, another boy behind him roared out, "No, ma'am."

"Why not?" asked the teacher.

"Because, when the thousand dollars are all gone, and all the things they've got with them are gone too, the lie is there all the same."

MAINTAINING OPINIONS

Galileo, who invented the telescope with which he observed the satellites of Jupiter, invited a man who was opposed to him to look through it, so that he might observe Jupiter's moons.

The man positively refused, saying, "If I should see them, how could I maintain my opinions which I have advanced against your philosophy?"

—*Albert L. Zobell, Jr.*
Story Sermons

MINE TO GIVE

During a war in Germany, the captain of a German cavalry unit found a man working in a field and asked him to show them a good barley field where they could feed their horses. The man promised to do so, and accordingly led them some way, until at last he brought them to what they were seeking.

"These will do very well," said the captain, and ordered his men to halt.

"Come a little further," said the man, "and I will show you a field that will do better." He led the troops further on, and sure enough, they came to another barley field.

"But this field isn't as good as the one you led us past," complained the captain.

"That is true," said the man, "but this field is mine and the barley is mine to give."

NOT A PENNY

Two noblemen had come before the king to request the governorship of a province in the kingdom. The king asked each how much he would pay for the governorship. Each named a price and then a bidding war began. The king suddenly stopped them, and asked a third nobleman, who was standing nearby, how much he would give for the governorship.

"Not a penny," answered the nobleman. "It's against my conscience to buy privilege."

"Then," said the king, "you of the three best deserve it." And he instantly conferred the governorship upon him.

PRESENCE OF MIND

One Christmas season, while a boy at school, I had saved up my money and purchased a pound of gunpowder. My parents being away, I went to the kitchen with my brother and two sisters. I poured the gunpowder into a large horn, with a wooden bottom and a cork for a stopper. There was about half a cup of gunpowder left, and my brother wanted it. I, however, didn't want to give it to him, and a fight resulted. He got so mad that he grabbed the powder horn and threw it into the fireplace where a fire was blazing. Fear paralyzed me. I couldn't move. I cried to my sisters to get out of the room. I began moving toward the door. My youngest sister, not knowing what was going on, ran toward the fireplace. I knew that the house would explode and we'd all be killed. My older sister, however, finally realizing what had happened, calmly but quickly walked to the fireplace, coolly took the tongs and removed the powderhorn, dumping it in a bucket of water that had been sitting by the kitchen door. It sunk to the bottom, hissed for awhile, then stopped. Without her presence of mind we would all have been killed.

—*Leifchild*

THE PRESIDENT OF THE CHURCH KEEPS HIS APPOINTMENTS

In Salt Lake City one Thursday, a Sunday School class had been granted the great favor of an appointment with the President. Unfortunately, he was called to the hospital where his brother Thomas E. lay critically ill. The children were naturally disappointed. A member of the Council of the Twelve greeted the class and talked with them.

Many busy men would have considered the matter closed, but the next Sunday morning found President McKay driving eight miles to a small chapel south of the city. Entering the building, he inquired where this particular class met. Imagine the thrill experienced in that little classrom when the door opened and the President walked in. After explaining why he was not in his office, he shook hands with the teacher and with each of the children and left his blessing.

"I want you children to know," he said, "that the President of the Church keeps his appointments if at all possible."

—Glenn Snarr

PROTECTION MONEY

During the Thirty Years' War in Europe, a German city offered the French military leader, Vicomte de Turenne, one hundred thousand crowns not to pass with his army through their city.

"Gentlemen," Turenne answered, "I cannot in good conscience accept your money, as I had no intention of passing that way."

SAVED BY INTEGRITY

Richard Jackson, a farmer, was arrested during the Revolutionary War and charged with planning to join the king's forces. He was too honest to deny this intention. Accordingly, he was turned over to the high sheriff and committed to the county jail. He could have easily escaped from the jail, but he considered himself in the hands of authority and prepared himself to receive the consequences.

After having been in jail for a few days, he asked the jailer to let him go out during the day to work, promising that he would return by nightfall. His integrity was so well known that he was immediately given permission. For eight months Jackson went out every day to work and came back to the jail faithfully at night.

In May the sheriff prepared to take him to Springfield where he would be tried for treason. Jackson told the sheriff that he could save himself the trouble and expense. Jackson would go by himself. The sheriff allowed this and Jackson set off for Springfield.

On the way, he was overtaken in the woods by a Mr. Edwards, a member of the council of Massachusetts, which at that time was the supreme executive body of the state. Mr. Edwards asked Mr. Jackson where he was going.

"To Springfield, sir, to be tried for my life."

In Springfield Richard Jackson was found guilty and condemned to death. He immediately appealed to the council for mercy. The evidence was presented to the council and the president put the question before the council of whether the pardon should be granted. The case, he said, was perfectly clear. The act was unquestionably high treason and the proof was complete. And if mercy was shown in this case, he saw no reason why it should not be granted in every other.

One by one the members of the council agreed with the president, until it came time for Mr. Edwards, the man who Mr. Jackson had met in the woods, to speak. Instead of delivering his opinion, he simply related the whole story of meeting Jackson in the woods. The council was moved by Jackson's integrity and decided that such a man certainly should not be sent to the gallows. Jackson was pardoned.

SEVEN YEARS HONEST

In a small town lived an old woman whose only income was the room and board paid by travelers who stayed with her. One evening, after some merchants who had been staying with her had left, she found a sealed moneybag which appeared full and which had evidently been left by one of the company. Since she had no idea who the men were or how to get in touch with them, she put the bag in a cupboard, to keep it until it should be called for.

She kept the bag for seven years and, though very poor, she resisted the temptation to spend the money herself.

At the end of seven years some merchants stopped at her house to spend the night. One asked another if he had ever been in this town before.

"Yes, indeed," he replied, "I remember this town too well. My being here once cost me several thousand dollars."

"How so?" asked his companion.

"In one of these houses I left a loaded moneybag."

"Was the bag sealed?" asked the old woman, whose attention had been aroused by the conversation.

"Yes, yes, it was sealed, and with this seal." He pulled a seal from his pocket.

"Well, then, you shall recover it," said the old woman.

"Recover it? No, I am too old to expect that.

The world is not that honest. Besides, it has been seven years since I lost that money. I wish I hadn't mentioned the subject. It depresses me."

"Just a moment," the woman said as she left the room. In a minute she returned with the bag.

"Perhaps honesty is not as rare as you think," she said as she handed the bag to the astonished merchant.

THE STORY OF A DIAMOND

A French nobleman named De Sancy once owned a very valuable diamond. Henry III, then king of France, was in a desperate financial situation. De Sancy loaned him the diamond to be used as collateral on a loan. De Sancy entrusted one of his most faithful followers to take the diamond to the king, but the messenger and the diamond disappeared, to the great consternation of both Henry III and De Sancy. A diligent search was made, but no clues to the mystery were turned up. So strong was De Sancy's confidence in the honesty of his servant that he felt convinced that some misfortune must have happened to him. At length he discovered that his follower had been waylaid and murdered by a band of robbers, and the body concealed in a neighboring forest.

De Sancy recovered the body and ordered it opened. To the astonishment of all but De Sancy himself, the treasure was discovered. The messenger, on finding himself without possible escape, had swallowed the diamond rather than let it fall into the hands of the robbers.

THE TURKISH POSTMAN

In the winter of 1828 a Turkish postman was sent some distance with a large amount of gold. The gold was carried in bags, and was given to the postman without the sender receiving any document as proof of the postman's receipt of the money.

The postman, on arriving at his destination, was told that he was short the equivalent of fifteen thousand dollars. The postman made no attempt to deny the charge, but immediately said, "I must have lost the bag and will therefore pay you as soon as I can raise the money."

After thinking of the loss, the postman returned by the road by which he had come, hoping to find the money. He had traveled nearly the whole distance, when he arrived, depressed, at a roadside inn where he remembered he had stopped for a few moments. The owner of the inn, upon seeing him, shouted out, "Hallo, sir. When you were here last you left a bag, which I suppose contains gold. You'll find it just where you left it."

The postman entered and discovered the bag of money which he had lost, evidently untouched, although it must have been left in plain sight for several days.

THE TWO FARMERS

Two neighboring farmers has a dispute respecting the right to a certain meadow, and they could come to no compromise. They decided to take the matter to court. On the day appointed for the trial, one of the farmers, having dressed himself in his Sunday finest, stopped off at his opponent's so they could go together. Finding his neighbor at work, he said to him, "Could you possibly have forgotten that the trial is today?"

"No," said the other, "I haven't forgotten. But I can't spare the time to go right now. I knew you would be there, and I'm sure you are an honest man and will say nothing but the truth. You will state the case fairly, and justice will be done."

And so it happened. The farmer who went to the trial stated both sides very clearly and fairly and the judge ruled in favor of the farmer who had not come. The farmer returned home and informed his neighbor of the decision.

WHO RULES CONSCIENCE?

When certain persons tried to persuade Stephen, king of Poland, to force everyone in the country who was not of his religion to embrace his religion, he said, "I am a king of men, and not of consciences. The rule of consciences belongs exclusively to God."

WORMS AND SIN

Two men were working one day at a shipyard. As they were preparing a piece of wood to go into the ship, they found a small worm about half an inch long.

"This piece of wood is wormy," said one. "Should we put it in?"

"I don't know—yeah, go ahead and put it in. No one will ever see it," said the other.

The wood was put in the ship.

The ship was finished and as she was ready to be launched she looked beautiful. She was launched and for a number of years sailed well. But on one voyage it was found that the ship had grown weak and rotten. Her timbers were eaten away by worms, but the captain thought he would try to get her home. He had a valuable cargo aboard ship and a great many people.

On the way home the ship ran into a storm. She rode it well for awhile, and then sprung a leak. There were two pumps on the ship, and they were kept constantly running, but the water came in faster than they could pump it out. The ship filled with water and sank, carrying passengers and cargo to the bottom of the ocean. Many people never saw home again, all because of a small piece of wood with a worm in it.

YOU CANNOT HURT ME

Chrysostom, an early Christian, was brought before the Roman emperor, who threatened him with banishment if he did not denounce Christianity.

"The world is my Father's house," said the Christian. "You can't banish me."

"Then I'll kill you," said the emperor.

"You can kill my body but my soul is safe with God," said Chrysostom.

"I'll take away everything you own," threatened the ruler.

"My treasure is in heaven, as is my heart," replied the Christian.

"Then I'll drive you away from man and you'll have no friends left."

"That also is impossible, for I have a Friend in heaven from whom you cannot separate me. There is nothing you can do to hurt me."

COURAGE

Courage is armor
A blind man wears;
The calloused scar
Of outlived despairs:
Courage is Fear
That has said its prayers.

—Karle Wilson Baker

IF

If you can keep your head when all about you
Are losing theirs and blaming it on you;
If you can trust yourself when all men doubt you,
But make allowance for their doubting too:
If you can wait and not be tired by waiting,
Or, being lied about, don't deal in lies,
Or, being hated don't give way to hating,
And yet don't look too good, nor talk too wise;

If you can dream—and not make dreams your
   master;
If you can think—and not make thoughts your
   aim;
If you can meet with Triumph and Disaster
And treat those two impostors just the same:
If you can bear to hear the truth you've spoken
Twisted by knaves to make a trap for fools,
Or watch the things you gave your life to, broken,
And stoop and build them up with worn-out
   tools;

If you can make one heap of all your winnings
And risk it on one turn of pitch-and-toss,
And lose, and start again at your beginnings,
And never breathe a word about your loss:
If you can force your heart and nerve and sinew
To serve your turn long after they are gone,
And so hold on when there is nothing in you
Except the Will which says to them: "Hold on!"

If you can walk with crowds and keep your virtue,
Or walk with kings—nor lose the common touch,
If neither foes nor loving friends can hurt you,
If all men count with you, but none too much:
If you can fill the unforgiving minute
With sixty seconds' worth of distance run,
Yours is the Earth and everything that's in it,
And—which is more—you'll be a Man, my son!

—Rudyard Kipling

A NATION'S STRENGTH

What makes a nation's pillars high
And its foundations strong?
What makes it mighty to defy
The foes that round it throng?

It is not gold. Its kingdoms grand
Go down in battle shock;
Its shafts are laid on sinking sand,
Not on abiding rock.

Is it the sword? Ask the red dust
Of empires passed away;
The blood has turned their stones to rust,
Their glory to decay.

And is it pride? Ah, that bright crown
Has seemed to nations sweet;
But God has struck its luster down
In ashes at His feet.

Not gold but only men can make
A people great and strong;
Men who for truth and honor's sake
Stand fast and suffer long.

Brave men who work while others sleep,
Who dare while others fly—
They build a nation's pillars deep
And lift them to the sky.

—Ralph Waldo Emerson

_____

PREPAREDNESS

One weapon I would keep
From the world's scrapheap
Of longbows and swords,
Of bayonets and guns—
One weapon for my soul's defense.

Leave me the sword of truth,
Swift and sharp and strong
To pierce the subtle lie
In militant word and song—
One weapon for this land's defense.

Throw all else on the scrapheap.
Only one weapon let us keep.

—Jean Grigsby Paxton

_____

THEY ARE SLAVES

They are slaves who fear to speak
For the fallen and the weak.
They are slaves who will not choose
Hatred, scoffing and abuse
Rather than in silence shrink
From the truths they needs must think.
They are slaves who dare not be
In the right with two or three.

—James Russell Lowell

_____

TO THE MASTER-BUILDER

The windows of the place wherein I dwell
I will make beautiful. No garish light
Shall enter crudely; but with colors bright
And warm and throbbing I will weave a spell,
In rainbow harmony the theme to tell
Of sage and simple saint and noble knight,
Beggar and king who fought the gallant fight.

These will transfigure even my poor cell.
But when the shadows of the night begin,
And sifted sunlight falls no more on me,
May I have learned to light my lamp within;
So that the passing world may see
Still the same radiance, though with paler hue,
Of the sweet lives that help men to live true.

—Author Unknown

_____

Judging and Criticism

THE CAT AND THE BIRD

A lady had a tame bird which she was in the habit of letting out of its cage every day. One morning as the bird was picking crumbs of bread off the carpet, the lady's cat, which always before showed great kindness for the bird, suddenly seized it and, with the bird in her mouth, jumped upon a table. The lady was alarmed for the safety of her bird, but, on turning around, discovered the cause. The door had been left open and a strange cat had just come into the room. After she shooed it out, her own cat came down from her place of safety and dropped the bird, without doing it the slightest injury.

A CURE FOR GOSSIPERS

Hannah More, a celebrated writer who died some years ago, had a good way of managing gossipers. When she was told anything derogatory of another, her invariable reply was, "Come, we'll go and ask if it's true." The effect was sometimes ludicrously painful. The tale bearer was taken aback, stammered out an excuse, or begged that no notice be taken of the statement, but the good lady was determined. She took the scandalmonger to the scandalized, to ask questions and compare accounts. It is not likely that anybody ever a second time ventured to repeat a gossipy story to Hannah More. One would think her method of treatment would be a sure cure for a scandal.

DANDELIONS AND GOSSIP

A woman had a habit of cruel gossip. She confessed her fault to her religious leader. He told her to find a ripe, fluffy dandelion head and to blow the seeds into the breeze, scattering them abroad. She did as she was told, then wondering, returned to the religious leader. To her amazement, he told her to go back and gather up the scattered seeds. She objected, saying, "The task is far too difficult." Then the religious leader explained, "It is still more difficult to gather up and destroy all the cruel stories which you have circulated about others. Any thoughtless, careless child can scatter dandelion seeds before the wind in a moment, but the strongest and wisest man cannot gather them again."

A DISTINGUISHED LUNATIC

Isaac Newton moved to a new home, and his new neighbor was greatly puzzled by his actions. A friend visited her one day, and she mentioned that "a poor, crazy gentleman had moved in next door. Why," she continued, "every morning he takes his seat in front of a tub of water in the sun, and spends hours blowing soap bubbles through a clay pipe. He's very likely at it now. Come and look at the poor lunatic."

The visitor followed her upstairs and, looking out of a window into the next yard, burst out laughing. "My dear lady," he said, "the person you suppose to be a poor lunatic is none other than Sir Isaac Newton, studying the refraction of light upon thin plates, which is beautifully seen on the surface of common soap bubbles."

Doubtless the woman was less hasty, thereafter, in laughing at what she did not understand.

DON'T JUDGE A BOY

Don't judge a boy because he wears shabby clothes. When Bell, the inventor of the telephone, first entered Boston, he wore a pair of yellow linen breeches in the depth of winter.

Don't judge a boy because his home is plain and unpretending. Abraham Lincoln's early home was a log cabin.

Don't judge a boy because of the ignorance of his parents. Shakespeare was the son of a man who was unable to write his own name.

Don't judge a boy because he chooses a

humble trade. John Bunyan, the author of *Pilgrim's Progress,* was a fix-it man.

Don't judge a boy because of physical disability. John Milton was blind.

Don't judge a boy because he stutters. Demosthenes, the great orator of Greece, overcame a harsh and stammering voice.

Don't judge anyone. Not alone because someday they may far outstrip you in the race of life, but because it is neither kind nor right.

FRANKLIN IN LONDON

When a boy, Franklin went to London, entered a printing office, and inquired if he could get a job as a printer.

"Where are you from?" inquired the foreman.

"America," was the reply.

"Ah," said the foreman, "from America! a boy from America wanting a job as a printer! Well, do you really understand the art of printing? Can you set type?"

Franklin stepped to one of the cases, and in a very brief space set up the following passage from the first chapter of the Gospel of St. John: "Nathaniel saith unto him, can any good come out of Nazareth? Philip saith unto him, come and see." It was done so quickly, so accurately, and contained a delicate reproof so appropriate and powerful, that it at once gave him character and standing with all in the office.

GALLOPING TO CRITICIZE

A man once visited an art exhibit where the artist was present for comments. The man picked up one picture that had been leaning against the wall, and began to complain loudly that the artist was silly to paint a horse sprawled on his back. The artist, hearing him, came over, took the picture from his hands, turned it over, and handed it back. "Excuse me, sir," he said, "you're holding it the wrong way. It's a horse galloping."

HANDLING CRITICISM

When a friend told Plato that the boys in the street were laughing at his singing, Plato replied, "Then I must learn to sing better." Another friend warned him that there were many who frequently criticized him. "It doesn't matter," he said, "I'll live so that no one will believe them." Another time he was told that a friend was speaking ill of him. Plato responded, "I'm confident he would not do it if he didn't have a good reason."

A HINT TO GRUMBLERS

"What a noisy world this is!" croaked an old frog, as he squatted on the banks of a pool. "Do you hear those geese, how they scream and hiss? What do they do it for?"

"Oh, they're just enjoying themselves," answered a little field mouse.

"Soon we'll have the owls hooting. What is that for?"

"It's the music they like the best," said the mouse.

"And those grasshoppers, they can't go home without grinding and chirping. Why do they do that?"

"Oh, they're so happy they can't help it," said the mouse.

"You find excuses for all of them. I believe you don't understand music, so you like awful noises."

"Well, friend, to be honest with you," said the mouse, "I don't greatly admire any of them. But they are all sweet to my ears compared with the constant grumbling croaks of a frog."

THE HUMMINGBIRD AND THE BUTTERFLY

A hummingbird met a butterfly and, being impressed with the beauty of the butterfly and the glory of its wings, the hummingbird offered to be its friend forever.

"I don't think so," said the butterfly, "for at one time you spurned me and mocked me and called me ugly."

"Impossible!" exclaimed the hummingbird. "I am always respectful of such beautiful creatures as you."

"Perhaps you are now," said the other, "but when you insulted me, I was a caterpillar. So instead I'll give you a piece of advice. Never insult the humble."

I AM JOHN FLETCHER

A Mr. Berridge once met a man from a small town in southern Utah. "I've heard of a man," said Mr. Berridge, "from your town who seems to be a pretty good man. Several people I know have said many good things about him. His name is John Fletcher. Do you know him?"

"Yes, sir, I know him intimately. And if those friends of yours knew him as well as I do, they wouldn't speak so well of him."

"You surprise me," said Mr. Berridge, "in speaking so coldly of a man in whose praise others have been so warm."

"I have the best reasons," answered the man, "for speaking of him as I do—I am John Fletcher."

I NEVER FORGIVE

John Wesley was on a voyage to Georgia with General Oglethorpe. General Oglethorpe began telling Mr. Wesley about a servant of his who had greatly offended him. "I never forgive," said the general.

"Then I hope, sir," said Mr. Wesley, "that you never sin."

JUDGING FROM APPEARANCES

"Hey, you old man, the train will start in a minute. Hurry up or we'll leave you behind."

The train was waiting at the station. The baggage master was busy with his checks. The men were loading suitcases and boxes. Men, women and children were rushing into the railroad cars, hastily claiming seats, while the locomotive snorted and puffed.

An old man, simply dressed, was standing on the platform of the depot. He was looking around him and seemingly paid little attention to what was happening. It was easy to see that he was lame. He looked neither rich nor influential.

The conductor gave him a contemptuous look, clapped him on the shoulder and called out, "Hey, Limpy, get on board or we'll leave you behind."

"Time enough," replied the old man and he resumed his casual, calm attitude. He took his time and as the train began to move, the lame man stepped onto the platform of the last car, walked quietly in, and took a seat.

The train had gone a few miles when the conductor appeared at the door of the car. Passing along, he soon discovered the old man he'd seen in the station. "Your ticket, quick!"

"I don't pay," replied the old man quietly.

"Don't pay!"

"No, sir."

"We'll see about that. I'll put you off at the next station," and he seized a valise which was over the head of the man.

"Better not be so rough, young man," returned the stranger.

The conductor released the luggage for a moment, and seeing that he could do no more then, passed on to collect the fare from the other passengers.

As he stopped at a seat a few seats away, a gentleman who had heard the conversation looked up to the conductor and asked, "Do you know who you were speaking to just now?"

"No, sir."

"That is Peter Warburton, the president of the railroad."

"Are you sure?" asked the conductor, trying to conceal his shock.

"I know him."

The young conductor's face turned a little red, but he controlled himself and went on collecting his fares as usual.

Meanwhile, Mr. Warburton sat quietly in his seat. None of those near him could tell by the expression of his face what he felt or what he would do. He had been rudely treated, taunted with his infirmity. He could revenge himself if he chose. He could tell the directors the simple truth, and the young man would lose his job at once. The president himself had worked his way up from an errand boy, so why should he tolerate a stranger's roughness?

Those who sat near waited for what would happen. Soon the conductor came back. He walked up to Mr. Warburton's side, took his books from his pocket, the bills and the tickets he had collected, and laid them in Mr. Warburton's hand. "I resign my job, sir," he said.

The president looked over the accounts for a moment, then motioning him to the vacant seat, said, "Sit down. I'd like to talk with you."

As the young man sat down, the president turned to him. In his face there was no angry feeling. He spoke calmly. "My young friend, I have no revengeful feelings to gratify in this matter; but you have been unwise. Your manner, had it been to a stranger, would have been injurious to the company. I might tell the directors this, but I will not. But in the future, remember to be polite to all you meet. You cannot judge a man by the coat he wears, and even the poorest should be treated kindly. Take up your books. I'll tell no one of what has happened. If you change your manners, nothing of this incident will be remembered. Your job is still yours if you'll work to improve it.''

KIND JUDGMENTS

A quiet man one evening was walking through a town when he came upon some people gathered around something on a street corner. The man drew nearer to see what they were looking at. It was a dead dog, with a leash around its neck, by which it appeared to have been dragged through the dirt.

One man pinched his nose. ''Oh, it stinks.''

Another said, ''How long will we have to look at his ugly thing?''

''Look at his torn hide,'' said a third, ''you couldn't get enough leather from it to make a shoe.''

''And his ears,'' said a fourth, ''all cut and bleeding.''

''No doubt,'' said a fifth, ''he deserved what he got.''

The man heard them and, looking compassionately on, said, ''He has the whitest teeth I've ever seen.''

LET THE ANGEL OUT

Michelangelo was walking with some friends through the streets of Florence, when, in an obscure corner, he discovered a large block of marble lying neglected and covered with dirt and rubbish. Although he was in his good clothes, he at once fell to work clearing away its filth and trying to lift it from the slime and mire in which it lay. His companions, surprised, asked him what he was doing. ''There's an angel in that stone,'' he replied, ''and I want to let it out.'' He had it moved to his studio, and there patiently, with mallet and chisel, he let the angel out.

LONG ENOUGH

A sacrament speaker rose to the pulpit and gave a very brief sermon. After the meeting he was approached by a friend who said, ''I liked what you said, but your sermon was far too short.''

''If you will practice what I preached,'' replied the speaker, ''you'll find that my sermon was quite long enough.''

THE OLD SACK OF BONES

As some boys were playing in a small park, a bus stopped in the road nearby, and the boys gathered around it to see the passengers. Their attention was drawn to one man who seemed to have great difficulty in getting off. When he had done so, they saw that he was deformed. His legs and arms were bent and crippled. The boys were so amused that they followed him, calling him names; and one of them, Charlie Purdy, tormented the poor man, calling him ''the old sack of bones.'' But soon they tired of this and returned to their park. When it began to get dark, they went to their homes. Charlie lived quite close, and as he entered the house he met his father coming in search of him.

''Here, Charlie,'' he said; ''I have been looking for you. I want to introduce you to the man who saved your life.''

They entered the living room; and imagine the boy's surprise when he beheld the crippled gentleman, who said to him in a kind voice:

''Come here, my boy; how much you have grown!''

Charlie, in his confusion, wished he were far away, as his father related to him that while he was a little boy this gentleman had saved him from drowning, had caught a cold because of it which developed into rheumatic fever, which crippled him.

Charlie felt awful.

PETER THE GREAT

When anyone spoke ill of another in the presence of Peter the Great, he would quickly interrupt him and say, ''Well, now, he can't be all bad. Tell me what you like about the man. It's easy to splash mud, but I'd rather help a man keep his coat clean.''

SAILOR'S DEFENSE

Admiral Hunter once endangered one of his ships, and a court-martial was called to try him. Evidence was given that the vessel had been seriously injured, and he was put on the defense. His answer was, "Gentlemen, all the evidence you have heard is true. But you have not heard the reason why the vessel was injured. I ordered the vessel to be turned around. Why? There was a man overboard, and I hoped to save him. And gentlemen, I believe that the life of a sailor is worth all the ships floating on the seas."

SARCASM AND CONVICTION

A woman, though a good member of the Church, had a quick, sarcastic wit which she loved to use to criticize whatever she didn't think was perfect. One Sunday she and her husband, who had been less than enthusiastic about going to church, were walking home from sacrament meeting. The woman began making some amusing and spicy comments about the speakers, criticizing this and that point and making fun of the way they spoke. She went on like this for some time before noticing that her husband had been entirely silent for some time. Looking over at him, she saw tears in his eyes. This sacrament meeting in which she had found so much fault had sent an arrow of conviction to his heart. The woman, who had been trying to get her husband enthusiastic in the Church, now felt the weight of the damage she may have done by her sarcastic criticism. In silence the two walked home.

THAT REALLY LOOKS A MESS!

The home teachers were visiting Sister Johnson, a woman in the ward who was known as a constant complainer. Sister Johnson was working on some embroidery. Elder Berry, not knowing anything about embroidery, could only see the underside of the work and said, "Sister Johnson, what are you doing there? That really looks a mess!" (Elder Berry wasn't known for his tact.)

Sister Johnson turned her work over and said, "Why Elder Berry! You're looking at the wrong side of it!" She showed him the beautiful handiwork from the right side. Elder Berry had to admit that the work, from his new view of it, did look nice.

Elder Berry thought for a moment, and then said, "And that, Sister Johnson, is your problem too. You're looking at the wrong side of God's workings with you. Down here we're looking at the tangled side of God's providence. But he has a plan—here a stitch, there a stitch, and in the end a beautiful work."

THIRTY YEARS' WORK

When Sir Thomas Lawrence had once painted a picture in half a dozen sittings, he was told with something of a taunt that he had very easily earned a thousand dollars in thirty hours of work. His answer was, "No, sir; not in thirty hours of work, but by the work of thirty years."

—*Dr. Conder*

TO EACH HIS OWN

Five men entered the same field. The geologist found various types of rock formations. The botanist found the many kinds of plants. The entomologist discovered butterflies, beetles, and other insects. The farmer found the variations in the soil. The poet saw the wind in the grasses, the warmth of the sun and the flight of the bird against the azure sky. Thus, each man found the thing he was looking for.

—*Indiana Farmer's Guide*

TOO FEW EYELETS

A famous painter was accustomed, when he had completed any one of his pieces, to expose it in some public place to the view of the passersby, and seat himself behind it to hear the remarks which were made. On one of these occasions a shoemaker complained that the painter had given the shoes in the painting too few eyelets. The painter, knowing the man must be correct, changed his painting. The next day the shoemaker criticized one of the legs in the painting, but then the painter jumped up and told him to confine his criticisms to that about which he knew something.

TWO PAINTERS

Two painters were employed to fresco the walls of a cathedral. Both stood on a scaffolding constructed for the purpose, eight feet from the floor. One of them was so intent upon his work that he became absorbed, and in admiration stood back from the picture, gazing at it with delight. Forgetting where he was, he moved backward slowly, critically surveying the work, until he neared the end of the plank upon which he stood. At this critical moment his companion turned suddenly and, almost frozen with horror, saw his friend's imminent peril. Another instant and the enthusiast would fall to the pavement below. If he spoke to him it was certain death; if he held his peace death was equally sure. Suddenly he regained his presence of mind and, grabbing a wet brush, threw it against the wall, spattering the beautiful picture with ugly blotches of paint. The painter flew forward angrily, but, noticing the terrified look on his friend's face, stopped. When his friend told him of the danger, he looked suddenly below, and then with tears of gratitude blessed the hand that had saved him.

WATCHING ONESELF

"When I was a boy," said an old man, "we had a schoolteacher who had clever ways of catching the students. One day he said to us, 'Students, I want you to pay closer attention to your books. The first one of you that sees another student idle, I want him to tell me, and I will take care of it.'

"'Ah!' I thought to myself, 'there is Joe Simmonds, that I don't like. I'll watch him, and if I see him look off his book, I'll tell.' It was not long before I saw Joe look off his book, and immediately I informed the teacher.

"'Indeed,' he said, 'How did you know he was?'

"'I saw him,' I said.

"'You did! And were your eyes on your book when you saw him?'

"I was caught, and I never watched for idle students again."

THE "WAX" APPLE

A lady who excelled in making wax flowers and fruit was often criticized severely by her friends, and her work decried, as she believed, unjustly. One day she showed them an apple, which they as usual found fault with. One complained about its shape. Another complained about its color. Each found something to complain about. When they had finished, the lady cut the apple and ate it.

YOU ARE BEN JONSON

Ben Jonson, the seventeenth-century dramatist, used to dress shabbily. Being informed that Lord Craven would be pleased to see him, Ben went to his mansion. The porter, not liking his looks or dress, refused to admit him. Rough language and much noise attracted the nobleman to the door.

"I understand," said Ben, "that your lordship wished to see me."

"*You*, friend! Why, who may *you* be?"

"I am Ben Jonson."

"No, no; you cannot be the great author who wrote the 'Silent Woman'? You look as if you could not say *boo* to a goose."

The dramatist, looking straight at the nobleman, with a comical air cried, "Boo! Boo!"

"I am now convinced," laughed his lordship; "you *are* Ben Jonson."

AN ALLEGORY

A little seed lay on the ground
And soon began to sprout.
"Now which of all the flowers around,"
It mused, "shall I come out?
The lily's face is fair and proud,
But just a trifle cold;
The rose, I think, is rather loud,
And then its fashion's old.
The violet is all very well,
But not a flower I'd choose;
Nor yet the Canterbury bell,
I never cared for blues."
And so it criticized each flower,
This supercilious seed,
Until it woke one summer hour
To find itself a weed.

—*Rev. Charles Naugle*

FABLE

The mountain and the squirrel
Had a quarrel,
And the former called the latter "Little Prig";
Bun replied,
"You are doubtless very big;
But all sorts of things and weather
Must be taken in together,
To make up a year
And a sphere,
And I think it no disgrace
To occupy my place.
If I'm not so large as you,
You are not so small as I,
And not half so spry.
I'll not deny you make
A very pretty squirrel track;
Talents differ; all is well and wisely put;
If I cannot carry forests on my back,
Neither can you crack a nut."
—*Ralph Waldo Emerson*

IN MEN WHOM MEN CONDEMN AS ILL

In men whom men condemn as ill—
I find so much of goodness still,
In men whom men pronounce divine—
I find so much of sin and blot—
I hesitate to draw the line
Between the two, where God has not.
—*Joaquin Miller*

JUDGED BY THE COMPANY ONE KEEPS

One night in late October,
When I was far from sober,
Returning with my load of manly pride,
My feet began to stutter,
So I lay down in the gutter,
And a pig came near and lay down by my side;
A lady passing by was heard to say:
"You can tell a man who boozes,
By the company he chooses,"
And the pig got up and slowly walked away.
—*Author Unknown*

THE MESSAGE OF THE BELLS

I looked upon the dreary waste
Of man's ambition, lust and fear:

I judged all mortals in my haste—
The New Year bells rang loud and clear!

I wept for all the wars of old,
I doubted every dream of peace,
I sighed for mankind's lust of gold—
The bells of New Year would not cease!

I saw the starving poor go down
Amid the battles of the strong;
I cursed the cruel, heartless town—
Again the bells burst into song!

They sang of peace, they sang good will,
They sang of love that soon must reign;
I mocked their song, but could not still
The flooding rapture of their strain.

And thus the bells ring on and on
In countless hearts that claim the Hope:
They hail the ever-coming dawn
Though all the nations darkly grope.
—*Thomas Curtis Clark*

THE OWL-CRITIC

"Who stuffed that white owl?" No one spoke
    in the shop,
The barber was busy, and he couldn't stop;
The customers, waiting their turns, were all
    reading
The *Daily*, the *Herald*, the *Post*, little heeding
The young man who blurted out such a blunt
    question;
No one raised a head, or even made a suggestion;
    And the barber kept on shaving.

"Don't you see, Mr. Brown,"
Cried the youth, with a frown,
"How wrong the whole thing is,
How preposterous each wing is,
How flattened the head is, how jammed down
    the neck is—
In short, the whole owl, what an ignorant
    wreck 'tis!
I make no apology;
I've learned owl-eology.
I've passed days and nights in a hundred
    collections,
And cannot be blinded to any deflections
Arising from unskillful fingers that fail
To stuff a bird right, from his beak to his tail.
Mister Brown! Mister Brown!

Do take that bird down,
Or you'll soon be the laughing-stock all over
    town!"
    And the barber kept on shaving.

"I've studied owls,
And other night-fowls,
And I tell you
What I know to be true;
An owl cannot roost
With his limbs so unloosed;
No owl in this world
Ever had his claws curled,
Ever had his legs slanted,
Ever had his bill canted,
Ever had his neck screwed
Into that attitude.
He can't *do* it, because
'Tis against all bird-laws.
Anatomy teaches,
Ornithology preaches,
An owl has a toe
That *can't* turn out so.
I've made the white owl my study for years,
And to see such a job almost moves me to tears!
Mr. Brown, I'm amazed
You should be so gone crazed
As to put up a bird
In that posture absurd!
To *look* at that owl really brings on a dizziness;
The man who stuffed *him* don't half know his
    business!"
    And the barber kept on shaving.

"Examine those eyes.
I'm filled with surprise
Taxidermists should pass
Off on you such poor glass;
So unnatural they seem
They'd make Audubon scream,
And John Burroughs laugh
To encounter such chaff.
Do take that bird down;
Have him stuffed again, Brown!"
    And the barber kept on shaving.

"With some sawdust and bark
I could stuff in the dark
An owl better than that.
I could make an old hat
Look more like an owl
Than that horrid fowl,
Stuck up there so stiff like a side of coarse leather.
In fact, about *him* there's not one natural
    feather."

Just then, with a wink and a sly normal lurch,
The owl, very gravely, got down from his perch,
Walked round, and regarded his fault-finding
    critic
(Who thought he was stuffed) with a glance
    analytic,
And then fairly hooted, as if he should say:
"Your learning's at fault *this* time, anyway;
Don't waste it again on a live bird, I pray.
I'm an owl; you're another. Sir Critic, good day!"
                                    —*James Thomas Fields*

Knowledge and Preparation

AVOIDING CONVICTION

An Italian gentleman at Paris, who believed that no one but Italians could sing well, refused to admit that an opera singer whom he had never heard could sing at all as well as the singers of Italy. He finally agreed to hear her sing. After listening for five minutes, he rose to leave.

"Please stay," said his friend, "and you'll see in a moment that we have good singers too."

"I know," said the Italian, "and that's why I'm leaving."

THE BRAHMINS AND THE LION

In a certain town lived four men who were friends. Three of them were very knowledgable, but they lacked everyday wisdom. The fourth lacked knowledge; all he possessed was everyday wisdom. One day they met together. What good are our talents, they asked one another, if we do not travel, if we do not gain the favor of kings, if we do not earn money? Before all else, let us travel.

When they had traveled for awhile, they came upon the bones of a lion. One of the men spoke:

"This is a good opportunity to exercise our knowledge. Here is a dead animal: let us bring it back to life."

The first said, "I know how to assemble the skeleton."

The second said, "I can provide the skin, the flesh, and the blood."

The third said, "I know how to give it life."

The first assembled the skeleton, the second provided the skin, the flesh, and the blood. The third got ready to give the creature life, when the man of everyday wisdom observed, "It is a lion. If you bring it back to life, it will kill us all."

"You are so simple-minded," said another. "I will not be the one to frustrate the workings of knowledge."

"In that case," replied the man of everyday wisdom, "wait a moment while I climb this tree."

When he had climbed the tree, the others brought the lion back to life. The lion rose up and killed the three of them. The man of everyday wisdom waited until the lion had gone away before descending from the tree and returning home.

—Panchatantra

DON'T STOP

Von Bulow, a famous pianist, once said, "If I stop practicing for one day I notice it in my playing. If I stop for two days my friends notice it. If I stop for three days the public notices it."

THE ECCENTRIC KIDD

Bishop Kidd was known as being rather eccentric. He frequently surprised his ward members by the way he did things. One day one of his ward members was busy in his shop when, right in the middle of his work, in stepped Bishop Kidd, without knocking or being announced.

"Did you expect me?" asked Bishop Kidd.

"No, sir," the ward member replied.

"What if I had been death?" he asked in a solemn, earnest tone, and out he stepped as suddenly as he had come.

A HARD NUT TO CRACK

My attention was arrested the other day by what I saw in the window of a little shop. Cages hung from wires and hooks, while their occupants seemed intent upon making the most of their limited space by leaping from side to side and from top to bottom. Attracted by an idle curiosity, I entered and accosted the proprietor.

"Well, my friend, you have quite a show of animals. This is a small menagerie in its way, is it not?"

"Yes, sir," answered the proprietor. "I call it

my theological shop. Possibly you may not think it, sir, but these birds and squirrels have a great deal of human nature in them. Here, now, is a cage with only one squirrel in it. He represents a large and respectable class of Christians. See how sleek and quiet he is."

"May I touch him? Does he bite?" I asked.

"Heavens no," said the proprietor, "He can't bite anything. He's what I call a thoroughly orthodox squirrel."

"How, then, does he survive?" I asked. "How does he crack those nuts in his cage?"

"He doesn't crack anything," replied the man. "He fumbles over the nuts, and waits until I get time to crack them for him. I'll tell you how this came about. He has been for some time the pet of a person who took great pleasure in preparing his food for him. In order to save the little fellow time and trouble, his master cracked all his nuts, and now the poor squirrel's teeth have grown out of shape, and can't possibly gnaw anything that is hard."

"Well, what has this to do with theology?"

"Oh, a great deal, as I shall now show you. He is just like a great many good people that belong to the Church. They depend upon somebody's feeding them with carefully prepared food. They live spiritually on the scriptures and the doctrines of the gospel, but these things have to be cooked before they are eaten. They let others crack all the hard questions and make them so palatable that they can believe without really understanding. They never think of thinking for themselves on any doubtful or knotty point. After awhile they lose the power to do otherwise, and so live on what others are pleased to feed them."

—*T. P. Wilson*

HOW DID I KNOW?

In the lexicon of youth there is no such word as *fail*. Remember the story of the boy who wanted to march in the circus parade? When the show came in town, the bandmaster needed a trombonist, so the boy signed up. He hadn't marched a block before the fearful noises from his horn caused two old ladies to faint and a horse to run away. The bandmaster demanded, "Why didn't you tell me you couldn't play the trombone?"

And the boy said, "How did I know?—I never tried before!"

—*Walt Disney*

HOW SHOULD WE DESCRIBE YOU?

"How should we describe you to others?" asked a disciple of Confucious.

He answered, "Say that I am one who would rather learn than eat, who forgets sorrow because he's so caught up in achievement, and who hardly has time to notice that he's getting old."

HOW TO LEARN

A Persian philosopher, being asked by what method he had acquired so much knowledge, answered, "By not allowing shame to prevent me from asking questions when I was ignorant."

JOHN ADAMS'S SCHOOL DAYS

When I was a boy I had to study Latin grammar; but it was dull, and I hated it. My father was anxious to send me to college, and so I studied the grammar until I couldn't stand it any longer; and going to my father, I told him I did not like to study, and asked for some other employment. It was against his wishes, and he was quick in his answer. "Well, John, if Latin grammar does not suit you, you may try digging ditches. Put your Latin aside and try that!"

This seemed a delightful change, and to the meadow I went. But I soon found digging ditches harder than Latin, and the first morning was the longest I ever experienced. That day I was glad when night came on. That night I made some comparison between Latin grammar and digging ditches, but said not a word about it. I dug the next day, and wanted to return to Latin at dinner; but it was humiliating, and I would not do it. At night, work conquered pride; and though it was one of the severest trials I ever had in my life, I told my father that, if he chose, I would go back to Latin grammar. He was glad of it; and if I have since gained any distinction, it has been owing to those two days working in that abominable ditch.

—*John Adams*

NEVER TOO OLD TO LEARN

An educated philosopher was reading in his study when a little girl, a neighbor's daughter, requested some burning coals with which to start her mother's fire. The doctor remarked, "But you have nothing to carry them in," and arose immediately to get a shovel to lend her. The child stepped forward to the fireplace, took some cool ashes in one hand, and placed some live coals on top with the other. The astonished doctor threw down his books, saying, "With all my learning, I should never have thought of that."

LEARNING AND DOING

Working as an ordinary hand in a Philadelphia shipyard was a man named John L. Knowlton. His peculiarity was that while others of his class were at bars or indulging in pleasure, he was incessantly engaged in studying mechanics. One of his companions bought a poodle, and spent six months teaching the dog to do a jig on its hind legs. Knowlton spend the same period in discovering some method by which he could saw out ship timber in a beveled form.

His companion taught his dog to dance, but Knowlton in the same time discovered a mechanical combination saw that enabled him to do in two hours the work that would occupy a dozen men an entire day. That saw was soon used in all the shipyards of the country. It cuts a beam to a curved shape as quickly as an ordinary sawmill saw rips up a straight plank.

Knowlton continued his experiments. He took no part in parades or target shootings, and in a short time afterwards he secured a patent for a machine that would turn any material into a perfectly spherical form. He sold a portion of his patent for a sum that was equivalent to a fortune. The machine was used to clean off cannon balls for the government.

When the ball came from the mold the surface was encrusted, and the ordinary process of smoothing it was slow and tiring. This machine, almost in an instant and with mathematical accuracy, peeled it to the surface of the metal, at the same time smoothing out any deviations from the perfect spheroidal form.

The same unassuming man invented a boring machine that was tested in the presence of a number of scientific gentlemen. It bored at the rate of twenty-two inches an hour through a block of granite, with a pressure of only three hundred pounds on the drill. A gentleman present offered him ten thousand dollars on the spot for a part interest in the invention in Europe, and the offer was then accepted.

The moral of all this is that people who keep on studying are sure to achieve something. Mr. Knowlton didn't consider himself by any means

brilliant, but if once inspired with an idea, he pursued it until he forced it into tangible shape.

MORE BITTER DEATH

A man was threatened with death if he did not deny Christ. "Life is sweet, and death is bitter," claimed his assailants.

"True," said the man, "life is sweet and death is bitter. But eternal life is sweeter; and eternal death more bitter."

THE PHILOSOPHER AND A FERRYMAN

A philosopher stepped on board a boat to cross a stream. On the passage he asked the ferryman if he understood astronomy.

The man looked astonished. "Astronomy? No, sir, never heard of it before."

The philosopher replied, "I am very sorry, for one quarter of your life is gone."

A few minutes after he asked the ferryman, "Do you know anything of mathematics?"

The boatman smiled, and replied, "No."

"Well, then," said the philosopher, "another quarter of your life is gone."

A third question was asked of the ferryman, "Do you understand physics?"

"Oh no, no; never heard of such a thing."

"Well, my friend, then another quarter of your life is gone."

Just at this moment the boat ran into a rock. The ferryman jumped up, pulled off his coat, and asked the philosopher, "Sir, can you swim?"

"No," said the philosopher.

"Well, then," said the ferryman, "your whole life is gone, for the boat is going to the bottom."

THE SAME SPEECH

"How do you feel today, Sister Smith?" asked the bishop of an old ward member.

"Not too good, bishop, not too good," she replied. "I'm getting old and my mind's clean gone."

"I'm sorry to hear that," said the bishop. "It sure is a bother not being able to remember things. As a matter of fact, I know how you feel. I've had a problem with my memory for quite a while."

"Oh bishop, how can you say that?" said the old sister. "I've heard you give the same speech in church now for fifteen years and you haven't forgotten a word of it."

THE SOUND OF INTELLIGENCE

At a dinner a man who knew a little but thought he knew a lot was monopolizing the conversation. No one could get a word in edgewise. One man at the table asked his neighbor if the man was as intelligent as he sounded.

"For all I know," said the neighbor, "he may be intelligent, but I have never heard intelligence make so much noise."

SUMMING UP THE DAY

When traveling in Europe, I was so full of excitement and enjoyment that I had not time to keep a journal; so I just put down under each date one single word—the name of the city, or the name of the picture, or the name of the mountain, or the name of the pass, or the name of some person whom I had met; and now I can go back over a month's travels, and, though there are but these single words, that whole history starts up when I look at them. If you regularly take a memorandum book at night, and think back through the day, and bring up before you what God has done for you, what He has shown you, what significant thing has happened, and put down the caption of it under the proper date, you will be surprised to find what a calendar your book will become at the end of every year.

—*Henry Ward Beecher*

THAT'S STATISTICS FOR YOU

Knowing of my interest in the subject, he (Roscoe Eardley) stopped me one day and said, "I have the latest story on statistics for you. We were coming from California by automobile and we had all been over the road a number of times and were somewhat bored with it, and as travelers often do to pass time, we began counting service stations. And we counted one for almost every mile along that almost eight-hundred-mile journey. But that is not the story. We were so busy counting service stations that we ran out of gas!"

I did not sympathize with him too much because he had already told me there was one

service station for about every mile. Then he said, "That's statistics for you. Where we ran out it was about fifteen miles to the nearest gas pump!"

—*Richard L. Evans*

TOO WINDED TO JUMP

Washington Irving tells us of a Dutchman who, having to leap a ditch, went back three miles in order to get a good run at it, and found himself so winded by the time he got to the ditch that he had to stop and rest before he had strength to jump.

TWO ARTS

A young man once went to Socrates for lessons in the art of public speaking. On being introduced to the philosopher he talked so incessantly that Socrates asked for double fees.

"Why charge me double?" asked the young man.

"Because," said the orator, "I must teach you two arts: the one how to hold your tongue, and the other how to speak. And the first art is by far the more difficult."

WHAT ARE YOU GOING TO DO?

"What are you going to do?" said an old man to a young man just entering upon life.

"I hope to complete my college education."

"And then what?" asked the old man.

"I'll get a good job and devote myself to it."

"And what then?"

"I'll marry as soon as I can afford it."

"And what then?"

"I'm sure I'll be busy enough educating and providing for my family."

"And what then?"

"Well, I guess I'll grow old."

"And what then?"

"I suppose when my time comes I'll die."

"And what then?"

There was silence. The young man hadn't looked that far ahead.

LEARNING

Learning itself, received into a mind
By nature weak, or viciously inclined,
Serves but to lead philosophers astray,
Where children would with ease discern the way.

—Cowper

NOT KNOWING WHY

The one who fights
Not knowing why he should
Does for his chosen cause
More harm than good.

—Richard Devon Walker

SCIENCE

Nature and nature's laws
Lay hid in night;
God said, "Let Newton be,"
And all was light.

—Alexander Pope

Love and Friendship

THE BETTER PHYSICIAN

Arcadius, an Argive, was constantly criticizing Philip of Macedon. Arcadius once entered into Philip's jurisdiction and Philip's friends reminded him that now would be an ideal time to get even with Arcadius. Philip, however, had Arcadius brought before him and showered him with gifts and kindnesses. Some time afterward word was brought to Philip that his old enemy had become one of his warmest friends, and did nothing but praise him wherever he went. On hearing this, Philip turned to his friends and asked with a smile, "Am I not a better physician than you?"

COMFORTING

A little girl came home from a neighbor's house where her little friend had died.
"Why did you go?" questioned her father.
"To comfort her mother," said the child.
"What could you do to comfort her?"
"I climbed into her lap and cried with her."

A COURTEOUS ELEPHANT

Emerson Tennent tells of an adventure he had in Ceylon while riding on a narrow road through the forest. He heard a rumbling sound approaching, and soon saw approaching an elephant, bearing on his tusks a large log of wood which he had been directed to carry. Tennent's horse, unused to these monsters, was frightened, and refused to go forward. The elephant, seeing this, evidently decided that he must himself get out of the way. But to do this he had to take the log from his tusks with his trunk and lay it on the ground, which he did, and then backed out of the road between the trees until only his head was visible. But the horse was still too timid to go by. The thoughtful elephant pushed himself farther back, until all of his body except the end of his trunk had disappeared. When Mr. Tennent succeeded in getting his horse by, the elephant came out, took the log up again, laid it across his tusks, and went on his way.

GETTING ALONG WITH PEOPLE

Some of my rules and ways of managing Indians:
1. I never talk anything but the truth to them.
2. I think it useless to speak of things they cannot comprehend.
3. I strive by all means to never let them see me in a passion.
4. Under no circumstances show fear.
5. Never approach them in an austere manner; nor use more words than is necessary to convey my ideas; nor in a higher tone of voice than to be distinctly heard.
6. Always listen to them.
7. I never allow them to hear me use any obscene language.
8. I never submit to any unjust demands or submit to coercion.
9. I have tried to observe the above rules for the past twenty years and it has given me a salutary influence wherever I have met with them. Many times when I have visited isolated bands upon business and have been addressing them in a low tone of voice around their council fires, I have noticed that they have listened with attention and reverence. I believe if the rules that I have mentioned were observed there would be but little difficulty on our frontier with the red man.

—Jacob Hamblin

A GIFT OF ICE

One of the most respected charities in New York City was the ice charity. In the street where the ice was given stood one morning in the burning sun and suffocating heat a long line of haggard men and women waiting for their portion of the desired gift. Everyone in the line, and they were mostly tattered women and children, had her own story of want and privation written upon her face.

But there was one woman at the end of the line who stood eagerly and silently watching the gradual shortening of the line. Her face and her clothes told a story of poverty and suffering. She had arrived on a run, late, and now, panting with her exertion, she calculated the length of the line and her chances of securing what she sought. At last, as she had feared, the supply of ice gave out, and two or three women ahead of her seemed to be as badly disappointed as herself. Silently she began to sob.

"Are you sure it's all gone?" she asked pitifully of the agent.

"I'm sorry, but I have no more to give."

"What are you crying for?" asked a harsh-voiced woman beside her, a great, burly creature who was just trudging off with her cake of ice carefully wrapped up in a basket. She had taken the last piece, and her face was radiant.

"Because I haven't any ice," came the pathetic reply.

The big woman looked down upon the little woman and said coldly, "Why didn't you come sooner, the way I did?"

"I couldn't leave my husband."

"You ought to. It's your own fault."

Then she began to walk away, while the little woman turned to go in the opposite direction.

In a moment the burly woman turned around. Her voice and words were harsh, but her heart was right. She had two babies at home suffering from the heat, and ice was everything to her. She hesitated, and then called out, "Is he very sick?"

Then came the story. Yes, the husband had met with a bad accident. He was in a high fever and called for ice—craved it above all things. His wife had saved a few pennies and spent them on peaches for him, expecting to have ice given to her. "I thought they'd do him good," she continued, "but it's ice he needs, and I wish I could trade them back again for the money or a piece of ice."

"Come with me," said the big woman, slowly, "and I'll give you mine. We are poor enough, heaven knows, but thank God I can still help the sick."

GOOD FOR EVIL

"Mamma," said Charley, "now that I have a new sled, what will I do with the old one?" His face wore a puzzled look for a little while, then a thought struck him. "Mamma, there's a chance to do something—real good, too. What's the use talking so much about a thing, and never doing it?"

"What, Charley?"

"Well, mamma, if there's any boy in the world I hate, that boy's Sim Tyson. He's always bothering and teasing me and all the other boys, either taking our things from us or pretending that he's going to. It never does any good to get mad because that's just what he wants. But better even than this, Sim does like sleds, and—well, maybe it's foolish—but I've half a notion to give that old sled to him. It might make him think, and so do him good. Wouldn't it, mamma?"

"Yes, it might," said the mother.

So Sim got Charley's sled, which pleased and touched him beyond everything, and they do say he is kinder than he was before.

HOME TEACHING

At the dedication of the Los Angeles Temple in March 1956—Tuesday morning, that was the beginning of the fifth dedicatory session—we were entering the temple when somebody said, "There is an elderly woman coming down the walk. Evidently she wants to see you." She was walking, but she had to be helped. We returned and met her just as she and her companions came up the steps leading to the north entrance of the temple. We shook her hand and greeted her and did as much as we could in that short, brief time, and to encourage her we said: "Are these your two fine sons?"

"No," answered the one on her left, "we are her ward teachers."

What a beautiful example of watching over the Church always! They knew that that elderly woman wanted to attend that service. I do not know what help they had to give her in order to bring her there; they had to get an automobile, probably. I do not know whether she had any sons. I know only what I have told you. But they were her ward teachers and they knew her needs.

—*David O. McKay*

I'M DOING MY BEST

A teacher once lost his patience with a slow student. The pupil looked up in his face and said, "Why do you speak angrily, sir? I'm doing the best I can."

Years afterward, the teacher used to tell the story to his children and say, "I never felt so ashamed of myself in my life. That look and that speech I have never forgotten."

———————

AN INJURY FORGIVEN

When I was a small boy, there was a black boy in the neighborhood by the name of Jim Dick. A number of us, one evening, began tormenting the poor boy by calling him "nigger" and other degrading names. The poor fellow appeared sad at our conduct and soon left us. Soon afterwards we decided to go ice skating. I discovered, however, that my skates were broken. My only option was to borrow Jim's skates. I went to him and asked for them. "Sure, Robert. You're welcome to them." When I went to return them, I found Jim sitting by the fire in the kitchen, reading the Bible. I told him I had returned the skates and was very thankful to him for his kindness. He looked at me as he took the skates and, with tears in his eyes, said to me, "Robert, don't ever call me nigger again," and immediately left the room. The words pierced my heart, and I burst into tears, and from that time resolved never to abuse a person again.

—*Robert Southey*

———————

LOOKING OUT FOR YOUR FRIENDS

A man was walking along a road when he was accosted by a terrier dog. The animal's movements were so unusual that the man's first impulse was to avoid him at all costs. The dog, however, at last made himself understood, and the man turned and followed him a few hundred yards. He was led to the banks of a canal where he discovered a small dog struggling in the water for his life, and nearly exhausted by its efforts to save himself from drowning. The man stooped down and rescued the dog while the terrier watched.

———————

LOVING TIME

A few years ago when I returned to teaching, I was assigned a first grade. I was a bit apprehensive, since always before I had taught upper grades.

One of my first actions was to eliminate the "Show-and-Tell" period, since I felt that the children who had something to talk about did not require practice in communication, and that the shy ones who needed to speak out were reluctant to do so.

One of the shy ones in the class was a small, curly-headed girl named Teresa. After my announcement, Teresa came to me with a request:

"Mrs. Silva, instead of 'Show-and-Tell,' can we have a loving time?"

I was not quite sure what she meant, so I asked her to explain. I hope the years will never allow me to forget her answer:

"Every once in a while you could lift us and give us a hug and we could tell you something important. It wouldn't take long."

So from that day on, whenever a child needed loving he would stand close to my desk and receive a hug, a pat, and a few moments of my undivided attention while he told me something important. We had such a good class that year... it was the year my students taught me.

—*Myrtle Silva*

———————

MEN JUST AS GOOD AS WE WERE

I remember certain dashing, wonderful men who, during World War II, used to brief the various units of the 101st Airborne Division which they were leading into battle. (The classic Leader's Oration before the Battle enjoyed a revival in airborne operations where the army, a short hour before the battle, could sit quietly on the grass one hundred miles from the enemy and listen to speeches.)

It was the high point of their careers, the thing they had been working and hoping and looking forward to all their lives—to lead a crack regiment or division into battle, and they made the most of it. The feeling of euphoria was almost overpowering. They were smart, sharp, vigorous, compelling, eager, tense, exuding optimism and even humor, but above all excitement. Invariably General Maxwell Taylor would end his oration with: "Good hunting!" It was wonderful, thrilling; you were ready to follow that man anywhere.

But before the operation was a day old, every man in the division was heartily wishing that he was anywhere else, doing anything else but that. Everyone knew in his mind and heart that he was not sent to earth to engage in this nasty and immoral business. The heroism and sacrifice were real. The situation was utterly satanic and shameful. The POWs we rounded up to interrogate were men just as good as we were, the victims of a terrible circumstance that the devil's game of power and gain had woven around them.

—*Hugh Nibley*
"Beyond Politics"

MY STICK IS MY OWN

Crossing a city street in the nineteenth century, a gentleman saw another man unmercifully beating a miserable bare-boned packhorse. Furious with the man's cruelty, the gentleman stopped him and reproved him.

The man, however, answered, "But it's my own horse. Can't I do with it as I please?" With that the man continued to beat his horse.

The gentleman, irritated by this brutality, clobbered the horse beater two or three times with his walking stick. The horse beater, surprised, dropped his whip and turned on the man. "What do you think you're doing?" he demanded. "What business do you have beating me with your walking stick?"

"Why," replied the gentleman, "my stick is my own. Can't I use it as I please?"

NO GREATER LOVE

Long ago the Austrians came upon the Swiss, intending to make slaves of them. Although the Swiss were outnumbered four to one, they fought valiantly. Again and again they attacked the Austrian forces, but were driven back each time. For the Austrians, standing shoulder to shoulder, held out their spears before them, making an iron fence that neither man nor horse could break through. One of the Swiss soldiers came upon a solution. Crying out, "Take care of my wife and children," he threw away his armor, rushed in upon the enemy, took as many spears as he could in his body, and fell down dead at the very moment he broke through the fence. The rest of the Swiss rushed in after him and the Austrians were soon put to flight.

NORTH AND SOUTH

A Union soldier was mortally wounded on a battlefield in Virginia. As he lay on the ground far from his comrades, conscious that his end was near, a dismounted Southerner, who had lost his horse, came by. The Union soldier called for help and pleaded with him to stop and say a prayer for him. The Southerner knelt at the side of the dying man and began to pray. As he uttered one tender plea after another, the Union soldier crept closer and closer, until he placed both arms around the neck of the praying man, and when the last words of the prayer were uttered, he was dying on the chest of the man who had been his enemy, but was now a brother in Christ.

PLAYING TRICKS

A young man was studying at a college. One afternoon he walked out with an instructor, and they chanced to see an old pair of shoes. They appeared to belong to a poor old man at work close by.

"Let's have some fun at his expense," said the student. "Suppose we hide his shoes and watch him from the bushes."

"I can think of a better trick than that," said the instructor. "You are rich. Suppose you put a silver dollar in the toe of each of his shoes, and then we'll hide and watch."

The young man did so. The poor man finished his work and went to put on his shoes. You can imagine his surprise when he stooped down to pick out what he thought to be a pebble and found instead a silver dollar. He was doubly surprised to find another silver dollar in the other shoe. And from the bushes both the student and instructor enjoyed watching.

RUSSIAN BEARS

A man in Russia asked about the method of catching bears in that country. He was told that to trap them a pit was dug several feet deep, and after covering it over with branches, leaves, and so forth, some food was placed on top. The bear, tempted by the bait, easily fell into the snare.

"But," he added, "if four or five happen to get in together, they will all get out again."

"How is that?" asked the gentleman.

"They form a sort of ladder by stepping on each other's shoulders and thus make their escape."

"But how does the bottom one get out?"

"Ah! these bears, though not possessing a mind and soul such as God has given us, still feel gratitude, and they won't forget the one who has been the chief means of getting them out. They fetch the branch of a tree, which they let down to their brother, enabling him to join them in freedom."

SATAN'S PERSEVERANCE

A young lady was speaking to a friend who had called upon her regarding a characteristic of her mother, who always had a good word to say to everyone.

"Why," she said, "I believe if Satan were under discussion, mother would have a good word to say for him."

Just then the mother entered, and was informed what the daughter had said, whereupon she quietly said, "Well, my dear, I think we might all imitate Satan's perseverance."

SEND A LITTLE SUNSHINE

A youngster with a mirror was seen throwing rays of sunshine toward the upper story of a house. An old man nearby was curious and asked why he was doing it.

"I'm throwing a little sunshine up in Johnny's room—he's my pal. He broke his leg last week and today is our championship baseball game and Johnny can't be with us—so I'm sending him a little sunshine to let Johnny know that we're still around."

—*C. Lease Bussard*

THE SMELL OF YOUR FRIENDS

A Chinese priest, seeing an old piece of paper on the ground, told his pupil to pick it up, which he did immediately.

"What paper is it?" asked the priest.

"It is," said the pupil, "what once enveloped some perfume. It has been thrown away, but still retains the odor."

Going farther, the priest saw a piece of string upon the ground, and told the pupil to pick it up.

"What string is it?" he asked.

The pupil said, "It has a smell of old fish, once tied with it."

"In the beginning," said the priest, "people are pure and without fault, but by frequent contact with others, they bring themselves happiness or misery. If one keeps the company of wholesome and wise and good people, he becomes wise and good. But if he befriends foolish or cruel people, he becomes foolish and unhappy. As with this paper, it continues to be fragrant from having once enveloped perfume. The string has become stinking, having once touched fish. In the choice of our friendship with others, we contract good and bad habits from them.

THE SPARROW'S FALL

Several years ago someone broke into the farm and stole the President's best saddles from the saddle house. One of these was a hand-carved Mexican saddle and was prized very highly by President McKay. When the unfortunate incident became known, a group of stake presidents in Weber and Davis counties presented him with the best saddle available, so that he could still enjoy riding his horses while in Huntsville. Care was taken that this new saddle was kept in a safe place. Other saddles were later purchased to replace the ones that were stolen, and these were kept in the saddle house, but under lock and key. One day during hot weather, when members of the family were at the home in Huntsville, two of President McKay's sisters were out for a drive and decided to check on things at the farm. They found the door to the saddle house locked, but one of the windows open. They immediately corrected what they felt was a bit of carelessness and went on their way with a feeling of satisfaction that another theft had been averted.

That afternoon President McKay drove up to keep an appointment at Huntsville, with barely enough time to return to Salt Lake City for a later engagement. Upon being told of the open window, he said, "I left that window open purposely because there is a bird's nest inside, and that is the only entrance the parent birds have to carry food to their babies. I think I shall just have time to run over.''

When the sisters said they would correct the mistake, he insisted on doing it, saying, ''I must pick up a halter that needs repairing, anyway.'' When he returned to the house after the two-mile drive, he said in his gracious way, ''It was just as I expected—one little bird was outside trying to get in, and the mother was inside attempting to get out.''

His kindness to everyone and to everything has given him a benign demeanor that is one of his great characteristics. It has made him more like the One who ''marks the sparrow's fall.''

—Jeannette McKay Morrell
Highlights in the Life of
President David O. McKay

SPEAKING OF LOVE

The devil once pretended to be a preacher and went up to the pulpit of a church where a large congregation was waiting for a sermon. He preached on the pains of hell, and drew so terrible a picture for them that the congregation began to tremble, and when they left the church, they went home fearful and panic-stricken. A certain man was there who recognized the devil for who he was. After the sermon he asked the devil how he could undermine his own kingdom this way?

''I didn't undermine it,'' was the answer. ''I spoke of the torments of hell, but, if you remember, I didn't say a thing about God's love. Where there is no love, there can be no power for good. I have not set a single soul a step nearer to heaven, and I know I have driven some to despair.

TALK MORE TO GOD

A lady once went to her bishop and complained that her inactive husband, no matter how much she lectured to him, was growing farther from the Church. She had done all in her power to persuade him to straighten out his life.

''Sister,'' said the bishop, ''talk more to God about your husband, and less to your husband about God.''

THERE IS ANOTHER MAN

During a heavy storm off the coast of Spain, a crippled boat was observed by a British ship drifting out of control. The ship immediately lowered a boat to investigate. When they arrived at the crippled vessel they found only one man on deck. He was shriveled and sick-looking. He was carried to the rescue boat. Just as the boat was preparing to return to the ship, the men in the boat noticed signs of life in the rescued man. They huddled around him, watching anxiously to see if he was coming to. As they watched, the weak man uttered, ''There is another man.'' Rescued himself, the first use the saved one made of speech was to try to save another.

THE ULTIMATE SACRIFICE

An engineer on a locomotive saw a train coming with which he would undoubtedly collide. He decided to stand at his post and slow up the train until the last minute, for there were passengers in his train. The engineer said to the fireman, ''Jump!'' The fireman jumped and was saved. The crash came. The engineer died at his post.

WARMING OTHERS

A traveler was crossing a mountain pass alone. The snow was deep and the man was very cold. He struggled bravely against the desire to lay down and fall asleep, but he was beginning to lose the battle. As his eyelids sagged, his foot struck something in the snow. He looked down and saw that it was another man, half-buried in the snow. The traveler immediately grabbed the man in his arms and began to rub him vigorously, trying to save his life. The traveler carried him as quickly as possible to the next town, rubbing him all the way to keep him warm. When they had reached the next town the frozen man was showing signs of life. Then the traveler realized that the effort he had made to save the life of another had brought back life and energy to himself and thus saved his own life.

THE WAY TO CONQUER

"I'll master it," said the ax, and his blows fell heavily on the iron. But every blow made his edge more blunt, until he stopped trying.

"Leave it to me," said the saw, and with his sharp teeth he worked backward and forward on the iron's surface until the teeth were all torn or broken. Then the saw fell aside.

"Ha! ha!" said the hammer, "I knew you wouldn't succeed. I'll show you how." But at the first fierce stroke of the hammer, his head flew off, and the iron remained as before.

"Shall I try?" asked a soft, small flame. But they all despised the insignificant flame. He curled gently around the iron, and embraced it, and never left it until it melted under his irresistible influence.

YOU MUST LIKE PEOPLE

Sam Foss liked to walk. He had wandered a bit too far today in the blazing sun, lost in his thoughts, and now suddenly he realized how hot and tired he was. The big tree at the side of the road looked tempting, and he stopped for a moment to rest in its shade.

There was a little sign on the tree, and he read it with surprise and pleasure. The sign said, "There is a good spring inside the fence. Come and drink if you are thirsty."

Foss climbed over the fence, found the spring, and gratefully drank his fill of the cool water. Then he noticed a bench near the spring, and tacked to the bench another sign. He went over to it and read, "Sit down and rest awhile if you are tired."

Now thoroughly delighted, he went to a barrel of apples nearby—and saw that here, too, was a sign! "If you like apples, just help yourself," he read. He accepted the invitation, picked out a plump red apple, and looked up to discover an elderly man watching him with interest.

"Hello, there!" he called, "Is this your place?"

"Yes," the old man answered. "I'm glad you stopped by." And he explained the reason for the signs. The water was going to waste; the bench was gathering dust in the attic; the apples were more than they could use. He and his wife thought it would be neighborly to offer tired, thirsty passers-by a place to rest and refresh themselves. So they had brought down the bench and put up the signs—and made themselves a host of fine new friends!

"You must like people," Foss said.

"Of course," the old man answered simply. "Don't you?"

—*Sam Walter Foss*

BREAD OF BROTHERHOOD

The course of each life must vary
As the flight of each falling leaf.
For some the journey is lengthened,
For some the journey is brief.
But praise to the one who travels
With eyes on the fields of good,
Who makes from each storm-wracked harvest
The bread of brotherhood.

—*Lucia Trent*

DARE I PASS BY?

If I could see
A brother languishing in sore distress,
And I should turn and leave him comfortless,
    When I might be
A messenger of hope and happiness—
How could I ask to have that I denied
In my own hour of bitterness supplied?

If I might share
A brother's load along the dusty way,
And I should turn and walk alone that day,
    How could I dare—
When in the evening watch I kneel to pray—
To ask for help to bear my pain and loss,
If I had heeded not my brother's cross?

—*Author Unknown*

DISARM THE HEARTS

In hearts too young for enmity there lies the way
    to make men free;
When children's friendships are worldwide
New ages will be glorified.
Let child love child, and strife will cease.
Disarm the hearts, for that is peace.

—*Ethel Blair Jordan*

ENCOURAGED

Because you love me I have much achieved,
Had you despised me then I must have failed,
But since I knew you trusted and believed,
I could not disappoint you and so prevailed.
—*Paul Laurence Dunbar*

GOD'S MERCY

There's a wideness in God's mercy,
Like the wideness of the sea;
There's a kindness in His justice
Which is more than liberty.

There is no place where earth's sorrows
Are more felt than up in heaven;
There is no place where earth's failings
Have such kindly judgment given.

For the love of God is broader
Than the measure of man's mind,
And the heart of the Eternal
Is most wonderfully kind.

If our love were but more simple,
We should take Him at His word,
And our lives would be all sunshine
In the sweetness of our Lord.
—*Frederick William Faber*

IF BUT ONE FRIEND

If but one friend have crossed thy way,
Once only, in thy mortal day;
If only once life's best surprise
Has opened on thy human eyes;
Ingrate thou wert, indeed, if thou
Didst not in that rare presence bow,
And on earth's holy ground, unshod,
Speak softlier the name of God.
—*Lucy Larcom*

IF YOU CAN SIT AT SET OF SUN

If you can sit at set of sun
And count the deeds that you have done,
   And counting find

One self-denying act, one word
That eased the heart of him that heard—
   One glance most kind,
Which fell like sunshine where it went,
Then you may count that day well spent.
—*Robert Browning*

LOVE THAT IS HOARDED

Love that is hoarded, moulds at last
Until we know some day
The only thing we ever have
Is what we give away.

And kindness that is never used
But hidden all alone,
Will slowly harden till it is
As hard as any stone.

It is the things we always hold
That we will lose some day;
The only things we ever keep
Are what we give away.
—*Louis Ginsberg*

THE MAN OF SORROWS

Christ claims our help in many a strange disguise;
Now, fever-ridden, on a bed He lies;
Homeless He wanders now beneath the stars;
Now counts the number of His prison bars;
Now bends beside us, crowned with hoary hairs.
No need have we to climb the heavenly stairs,
And press our kisses on His feet and hands;
In every man that suffers, He, the Man of
   Sorrows, stands!
—*Author Unknown*

TORMENTED SORELY BY THE CHASTENING ROD

Tormented sorely by the chastening rod,
I muttered to myself: "There is no God!"
But, faithful friend, I found your soul so true,
That God revealed Himself in giving you.
—*Walter Malone*

Missionary Work and Teaching

ALL THE WAY TO GREAT BRITAIN

An Englishman bought a farm in Utah's Davis County. He was not a member of the Church, but all his neighbors were, and when they met this English neighbor they did not want to impose their religion on him and so they passed the time of day and talked about current events.

Finally one of these neighbors was called on a mission to Great Britain, and while he was over there, his English friend decided to go back and visit his relatives in England. While there he picked up a newspaper one evening, and there he read an announcement about a Mormon conference to be held. "Everyone invited—no collection," read the advertisement.

"Well," the visiting Englishman told his relatives. "After living among them for all these years, I do not know a thing about what they believe. I think I'll go and listen to them."

So he went, and to his surprise, the principal speaker that evening was his next-door neighbor in Davis County. He had to go all the way back to Great Britain to get that neighbor to tell him about the marvelous work and a wonder that the Lord had set his hand to do in our day.

—*LeGrand Richards*

FLYING FOR HIGHER GAME

While on my first mission in the Eastern States I was asked:

"Why don't you 'Mormon' elders fly for higher game? Why do you always preach to the poor and lowly? Why don't you get up among the high and mighty? Take Henry Ward Beecher, for instance. Convert him, and his whole congregation would flock in after him; and just see how that would build up your Church."

"That is not God's way of building up His Church," I replied. "The Lord declared by an ancient prophet, 'I will take you one of a city, and two of a family, and I will bring you to Zion: And

I will give you pastors according to mine heart.' " (Jeremiah 3:14-15.)

I explained the great problem of the dispersions and gathering of Israel, whereby the blood of Abraham, Isaac, and Jacob, the blood that believes, with spirits answering to that blood, who have been dispersed for a wise purpose among all nations, are now being recalled and brought together in a great movement called "The Gathering," preparatory to the building of the New Jerusalem and the glorious coming of the Lord.

And I added, "God is not anxious for great congregations. He is not desirous that any one person or people should make a bargain with Him and join His Church as a business proposition."

—*Orson F. Whitney*

GETTING ON COMMON GROUND

Before we can teach, we must get on common ground, with love and genuine understanding of the heart.

I was speaking to a man and his wife who had come to Temple Square. The man said: "I am a Lutheran."

I had the pleasure of saying to him, "I remember what Luther taught his people: 'I believe it takes the truth of the heart and soul to understand the truths of God.' "

My newfound friend replied: "I believe that." And continuing, he asked, "You are a great admirer of Luther?"

"Yes, very much so."

And then as we stood there on Temple Square, the conversation turned to the restoration of the Church. When he left later, he took me by the hand, saying, "Friend, I am now an admirer of Joseph Smith, who, you say, is a prophet of God."

You see, we came on common ground, and he felt happy that we found something good in his belief, and I felt happier that he found something noble in mine.

—*Levi Edgar Young*

HAVE A GOOD TIME

"Have a good time." That was the slogan we had in the West European Mission: Have a good time. I would like you all to have a good time.

I said this to a group of missionaries in Germany one day. After the meeting, one of the missionaries came up to me and he said, "President Tanner, I don't think that it is quite fair for you to tell the missionaries to have a good time. You know, the only way they can have a good time is to do their work."

I said, "Well, go have a good time."

—*N. Eldon Tanner*

JOHN CODMAN AND THE MORMON MISSIONARIES

I was talking once with Captain John Codman, who owned a sailing vessel before the time of steam. He had sailed over many seas. He had had all kinds of adventures and experiences and was acquainted with all kinds of people. He also had become quite a noted magazine writer, furnishing articles to many of the leading magazines of the country. Finally he suffered from asthma, and he discovered he was better at Soda Springs, Idaho, than at any other place. And having an abundance of money, he bought four or five houses, bought a little cottage there, and used to come to Soda Springs just as early as he could in the spring and stay just as late as he could on account of the cold and snows.

He averaged spending about seven months a year at Soda Springs, and I became acquainted with him here in Salt Lake City; had some business dealings with him, and it so happened that the money that he placed in my hands as a young man of twenty-two or -three, to invest for him, turned out very well. In one investment of about two thousand dollars, he made some twenty thousand out of it, and we became very familiar.

During the three years at Soda Springs every summer with a sick wife, I became quite intimate with him, and he said to me once, "Grant, the greatest education in the world comes from your missionary system. Why," he said, "there is

nothing like it. I am convinced that the average Mormon boy who goes out for three years to proclaim your gospel comes home improved better than he would have been if he had gone through the best university in all the world. There is nothing like it. I never was more astonished in my life than to discover the growth in your young men who go out as missionaries."

He gave me an example. He said, "There was my stable boy, currying my horses. Why, when I heard he was called on a mission to Germany, I laughed and said, 'That boy will never even learn the German language, I am sure.' He had been away about a year and a half when I got a letter from him. He had run across some of my relatives over there who had gone to Germany to live for a few years to put their children in school to get certain education and to acquire the German language practically, by coming in contact with the actual Germans. When he heard they were relatives of mine, he thought he would get a letter of introduction from me to them, and I thought of what my cultured relatives would think of him, and I said, 'I am not going to give the ignoramus a letter.' But afterwards I thought if he was fool enough to ask for it, I would give it to him. So I sent it.

"Pretty soon I got a letter in answer from my folks, thanking me for introducing the young Mormon; that he was a very bright, intelligent young fellow, and they had thoroughly enjoyed his visit.

"I decided when he returned home I would go and hear him preach. I thought it would be a joke. He came home in another year and a half, and I went to hear him speak. He gave as logical a sermon and made his points from the standpoint of your faith as well as anyone could. Why, he was way ahead of fellows who go to theological seminaries for years, and I was astonished. Now I always go to hear the boys from Soda Spring when they come back from missions. I have never been disappointed. It is wonderful."

I said, "It is not so wonderful when you stop to think that they are taught by the inspiration of the Lord."

He said, "Rubbish, rubbish."

"Well," I said, "you say they progress more rapidly than in the finest universities in the world; where do they get the progress, if it is not from the Spirit of the living God that attends them in their labors?"

—*Heber J. Grant*

THE LAMPLIGHTER

I stood one day in far-off France with a group of boys about me. The colorful old lamplighter came with his interesting cape and his stiff-brimmed hat. He started to light the lamps. He lit this one; then he crossed the way and lit another. Then again, and this one did not burn very easily; he had to go up the post and clean it out. He was patient, and finally the light came on. We smiled, and he crossed the way again. By and by down the highway he went, and over into the city, and came again on the distant hilltop. We watched with great interest to see this great pathway of light—one man lighting the highway. And so it may be with us in our missionary service. It may be difficult here or there. The light may not come on very easily, but with patience, with constant striving, and with prayer in our hearts, the highway will be made light, a safe place to travel.

—Oscar A. Kirkham

MAKE THEM BELIEVE

"How is it," demanded a preacher of a great actor, "that I, in teaching divine doctrines, produce so little effect upon my congregation, while you can so easily rouse the passions of your listeners by speaking fiction?"

"Because," responded the actor, "I recite falsehoods as if they were true, while you deliver truths as if they were fiction."

ONLY TWO

A missionary, on returning from his mission, was asked how many people he converted. "Only two," he said, "and they soon went inactive."

The questioner was about to give his condolences when the missionary continued. "But the Lord converted many. And today they're stronger in the Church than ever."

PATIENCE IN TRIAL

In July of 1914 two humble elders one evening about ten o'clock were seeking some kindhearted Christian who would shelter them for the night. There was a lady engaged on the lecture platform, going from city to city in that section, warning people against the preaching of the Mormon elders. These two young men from Utah unwittingly called at the home where this lady was staying, and asked for entertainment. The man of the house met them, and turning to those within the house, he said:

"Here are two Mormon elders now; speak of the devil and he is close by."

His wife said, "Call them in; I would like to look at a Mormon."

The woman lecturer said to them, "I am out on an errand against you. I am surprised that you should befoul our Christian atmosphere by your presence. I, too, wanted to have a look at you."

After she had looked at them for a moment, she went out of the room, suspiciously satisfied. They were told that they could not remain, but were called in only to be objects of scorn.

One of the elders said: "My good friend, we are very tired. We have traveled all day without lunch or dinner, and we feel that we can't go any further. Do you have any objections to our sleeping in your barn tonight?"

The man said: "I suppose there is no objection to your going out to sleep in the barn where the cattle are, and I will give you two quilts."

They went out into the barn, into a hay mow, but before retiring the two elders lifted up their voices in song, singing, "Come, come, ye Saints, no toil nor labor fear . . ." and including the verse, "Why should we mourn, or think our lot is hard? 'Tis not so, all is well."

Then they knelt down and prayed that the blessings of the Lord might be upon the owner of the place, that he might always hold his property in peace for administering to the wants of God's servants.

When they had finished praying, they heard someone outside the barn. The man and his wife and the woman who had come to lecture against them had stolen out to see what manner of mischief the Mormon elders might do, and they had heard the sermon of their lives.

The result was that the woman who was once so bitterly opposed to the Church began investigating the gospel.

—Walter P. Monson

THE SHEEP KNOW THE SHEPHERD

A man in India was accused of stealing a sheep. He was brought before the judge, and the supposed owner of the sheep was present. Both claimed the sheep, and had witnesses to prove their claims, so it was not easy to decide to whom the sheep belonged. Knowing the habits of the shepherds and the sheep, the judge ordered the animal to be brought into court, and sent one of the two men into another room, while he told the other to call the sheep, and see whether it would come to him. But the poor sheep, not knowing the voice of a stranger, would not go to him. In the meantime, the other man in the adjoining room, growing impatient, gave a kind of a "chuck," upon which the sheep bounded away towards him at once. This "chuck" was the way in which he had been used to call the sheep, and it was at once decided that he was the real owner.

THEY WENT BAREFOOT

A poor bishop in a small town tried to persuade a neighbor family, which had such vagrant habits that they almost deserved to be called a family of tramps, to settle down, live decently, and attend church.

"At least," he said to the mother, "let the boys come to Sunday School."

"They have no clothes fit to wear," she said.

"I'll find clothes for them," he answered.

The bishop, with much sacrifice, was able to find the clothes.

"They won't go barefoot," said the mother. "I won't have my boys laughed at."

The bishop could not afford shoes. His pockets were empty. He thought a moment.

"My own boys will go barefoot," he said, "then yours won't be laughed at."

"What do you say, Jack, Tom?" he said a few hours later at the supper table. "Will you go barefoot to bring these boys to church?"

Jack and Tom laughed, and finally consented.

The other boys went to Sunday School for a few months, and then the entire family disappeared, and the bishop soon forgot about them.

Several years later the good bishop, now an old man, was visiting a ward in another state, and after the meetings were over the bishop of the ward came up to him. He was one of the vagabond boys.

"All that I am I owe to that kindly thought of yours about the shoes," he said. "It was the first act of self-sacrificing kindness that ever had come

into my life. It turned me to a new path of thought and action, and the good influence of the Sunday School did the rest. Your boys probably thought it was a little thing to go barefoot for a few Sundays. But it saved a human soul."

TOO MUCH MILK

A man moved into a small farming community and was soon made bishop. He was humbled by the calling and felt the responsibility that came with it. Accordingly, he would frequently get up before the congregation and give lengthy sermons on various aspects of the gospel that he felt his ward needed help with. Many times he would take an entire meeting preaching on one subject. But because of his efforts at "feeding his flock," he was dismayed to see many ward members yawning or falling asleep during his sermons. As he walked along a dirt road one day, thinking about this problem, he came upon a dairyman, a member of his ward, who was walking in the same direction. Feeling like he needed to talk to someone about his worries, he stated the problem to the man and asked him what he thought of it.

"Well, bishop," the dairyman said, "you've been good for us since you've been made bishop, and we appreciate it. We're obliged for your intentions and know that what you tell us is good, but you preach too long! Speaking for myself, I'm a lot like my milk cans. You can put only so much in one of those cans and then it will hold no more. And once it's filled to the brim, if you try to put any more in, even if it's the best milk in the world, it will only be spilled on the ground and wasted."

HEAVEN'S GATE

Heaven's gate is shut to him who comes alone;
Save thou a soul, and it shall save thy own.
—*John Greenleaf Whittier*

INFLUENCE

A Persian fable says: One day
A wanderer found a piece of clay

So redolent of sweet perfume,
Its odor scented all the room.

"What art thou?" was the quick demand,
"Art thou some gem from Samarcand
Or spikenard rare in rich disguise?
Or other costly merchandise?"

"Nay, I am but a piece of clay."
"Then whence this wondrous sweetness, pray?"
"Friend, if the secret I disclose,
I have been dwelling with a rose."

—*Author Unknown*

Money and Charity

A CREDIT REFERENCE

A New York firm applied to Abraham Lincoln, some years before he became President, for information as to the financial standing of one of his neighbors. Mr. Lincoln replied as follows:

"I am well acquainted with Mr. X, and know his circumstances. First of all, he has a wife and a baby; together they ought to be worth fifty thousand dollars. Secondly, he has an office in which there is a table worth one and a half dollars, and three chairs worth, say, one and a half dollars, and three chairs worth one dollar. Last of all, there is in one corner a rat-hole, which will bear looking into. Respectfully yours, A. Lincoln."

—The San Francisco Argonaut

THE DAUGHTER'S INHERITANCE

The bishop was interviewing members of the ward to determine the amount of their donations to the ward budget and the building fund. There was one woman in the ward, a widow, whose daughter had recently died. The bishop knew that she was in no condition to donate, but he still called her in for an interview, hoping to console her and to show her that though she could not donate, they were still thinking of her.

During the interview the bishop, as a formality, asked the woman if she thought she would be able to make any donations. At this, the woman brought out a check, drawn from a local bank for a large amount of money.

"We can't take this, sister. You need it more than the Church."

"You must take it all. I had saved this up for my daughter and I am determined that He who has my daughter should also have her inheritance."

FINDING WORK

A beggar once came to the house of a kind man looking for a donation or for work. The man thought for a moment and then said, "I'll give you five dollars if you'll take this wood in the front yard into the back yard."

This the beggar was glad to do, and the job took him about an hour. When the job was done he returned to the kind man and asked if there was anything else he could do.

The man thought for a moment and then said, "If you bring the wood in the back yard into the front yard I'll give you another five dollars."

THE GENEROUS GIVER

I remember, upon one occasion—having had placed upon me by the Presidency of the Church a somewhat difficult mission to raise a large sum of money in the way of donations to maintain the honor and credit and good name of certain prominent men—receiving a letter from one man saying that he heard I was engaged in this financial mission, and he said he rejoiced to hear of it, that he had long wanted the opportunity of doing something, in addition to his tithing, to show to the Lord his appreciation of the wonderful blessings that had come to him. He concluded: "I have pleasure in sending you five thousand dollars to assist in this mission that has been placed upon you, and if you need more from me, do not hesitate to call."

I could not help contrasting in my feelings the position that this man took with that of a president of a stake to whom I appealed for one thousand dollars, and who, I am sure, was worth at least twice as much as the man who, without solicitation, had sent me a check for five thousand dollars. He not only did not give me anything at all, this stake president, but he made it his special business to see the men of means in his stake and forestalled my visit there so that when I went there I did not get anything from anybody.

—Heber J. Grant

A GOOD HEART

A boy was eating a stale sandwich on a street corner, when a stray dog came along and crouched at his feet. The hungry look remained in the boy's eyes, but he glanced down at the vagabond dog, and said in a friendly way:

"What you want? This ain't no bone. Git!"

The dog moved off a little, and again it crouched and looked at the food.

"Say, do you want this sandwich?" asked the boy, "Speak, can't you?"

The dog gave a quick bark, and the boy threw him the rest of the sandwich.

"Enough said," he remarked, as he watched him eat ravenously. "I ain't the kind to see a friend in trouble."

And the boy went off one way and the dog he befriended another, both the better for the encounter.

THE KING'S CHARITY

Antigonus, king of Syria, had tremendous charity. One day, when seated in a tent in the camp, he heard some soldiers who did not know that he was near them speaking ill of him. But instead of summoning them to appear and answer for their words and suffer punishment, Antigonus drew aside the curtain of his tent and said, "Men, you may want to go somewhere where your king can't hear you."

THE MAGIC BED

There was a man who owed a great deal of money, yet could sleep soundly. When the king found out about this he sent to buy the bed, figuring that since it couldn't be the man's conscience that was letting him sleep, it must be something magical about the bed.

THE MISER OF MARSEILLES

An old man lived and died in the town of Marseilles, France. He had worked very hard, been very thrifty, and had acquired a large amount of money. His neighbors considered him a miser, and thought that greed was causing him to hoard his money. Whenever the man went outside, boys would follow him, calling him names. He at length died, and in his will were found the following words: "Having observed from my infancy that the poor of Marseilles are ill supplied with water, which can only be purchased at a great price, I have cheerfully worked my whole life in order to help them with this problem, and I direct that the whole of my property should be used in building a water system for their use."

MR. COBB'S COVENANT

In 1821, Nathaniel Ripley Cobb, a Boston merchant, decided that instead of acquiring wealth for himself, he would dedicate any excess to the Lord. He therefore drew up the following document:

"By the grace of God, I will never be worth more than fifty thousand dollars.

"By the grace of God I will give one-fourth of the net profits of my business to charitable and religious uses.

"If I am ever worth twenty thousand dollars, I will give one-half of my net profits; and if I am ever worth thirty thousand dollars, I will give three-fourths; and the whole after fifty thousand dollars.

"So help me God; or give to a more faithful steward, and set me aside. N. R. Cobb, November, 1821."

He adhered faithfully to this covenant. At one time, finding his property had increased beyond fifty thousand dollars, he at once gave the surplus, seventy-five hundred dollars, to a local university to establish a professorship. Several times during his life he gave away much more than that. He was a generous friend to many.

MRS. HOWARD'S SPENDING MONEY

John Howard was a generous philanthropist. At the end of a particular year he settled his accounts and found that he had a little money left over. As a treat to his wife he suggested that they use the money to take a trip to Europe.

His wife was sitting on a couch knitting. Without looking up from her work she stated,

"What a nice little home for a poor family that money would make."

John Howard took the hint and used the money for that purpose.

NOT RICH BUT GENEROUS

A poor workman was sitting on a street corner eating his lunch. A poor, ragged woman was standing a little distance from him and watching him closely.

The workman noticed her staring and asked her what she wanted.

Pointing to his meal, she replied, "I haven't eaten so much as that in two weeks."

"Well, sit down here and take a bite," said the kindhearted workman. "I ain't rich, but I'm generous."

THE POOREST MAN

A shrewd old gentleman once said to his daughter, "Be sure, my dear, you never marry a poor man; but remember that the poorest man in the world is one that has money and nothing else."

A RICH MAN ON RICHES

Jacob Ridgway, a wealthy citizen of Philadelphia who died many years ago, leaving a fortune of several million dollars, was approached by a young man. "Mr. Ridgway," he said, "you are more to be envied than any man I know."

"Why so?" responded Mr. Ridgway. "I'm not aware of any cause for which I should be particularly envied."

"What, sir!" exclaimed the man in astonishment. "Why, aren't you a millionaire? Think of the thousands your property brings you in every month!"

"Well, what of that?" replied Mr. Ridgway. "All I get out of it are my food and clothes; and I can't eat more than another, or wear more than one suit at a time. Can't you do that much?"

"Ah, but think of the fine houses you own, and the money they bring you!"

"What good does that do me? I can only live in one house at a time; as for the money I receive for rents, I can't eat it or wear it. I can only use it to buy other houses for other people to live in. They are the beneficiaries, not I."

"But you can buy splendid furniture, and costly pictures, and fine cars—in fact, anything you desire you can have."

"And after I have bought them," responded Mr. Ridgway, "what then? I can only look at the furniture and pictures, and the poorest man who is not blind can do that. I can ride no easier in a fine car than you can in a bus for five cents, without the trouble of attending to other drivers and gasoline and taxes. And as to anything I desire, I can tell you, young man, that the less we desire in this world, the happier we shall be. All my wealth cannot buy me back my youth, cannot purchase exemption from sickness and pain, cannot give me power to keep off death. And then, what will it avail when, in a few short years at most, I lie down in the grave and leave it all forever? Young man, you have no cause to envy me."

THE SHOESHINE'S GIFT

I was passing along a busy street as two shoeshine boys were at dinner. With the sidewalk for their table, and a couple of thick slices of bread and meat to eat, they seemed quite content, and ate with a hearty relish. When about half done one of them made a sudden stop. Whispering a few words to the other, he gathered up the remaining half of their dinners, ran after a poor beggar, gave it to him, and then, with a happy face, returned to his work.

—*Hand and Heart*

SOMETHING IN THE BUILDING

A new church was being built and an old woman came up to the person in charge of raising funds and offered her small donation.

"But you don't need to offer anything," said the fund-raiser. "You need the money more yourself."

"It's true that I only have a little to give," said the woman, "but I consider it a privilege and an honor to have something, even if it's a single nail, in a building in this city that is dedicated to Christ."

SORTING THEM OUT

John Frederic Oberlin was noted for his charity and benevolence, but he had a good way of determining just who was worthy of his benevolence. Whenever a beggar would come to his door he would ask him, "Why don't you work?"

"Because no one will hire me," was the usual answer.

"Well, then, I'll hire you. There—carry these planks—break those stones—fill that bucket with water, and I will pay you for your trouble."

This sorted out the honest from the dishonest. The honest would gladly go to work, while the dishonest would make some excuse and leave as fast as they could.

THE UNEXPECTED DONATION

When the money to build Bethlehem hospital was being collected, those who were employed to solicit donations went to a small house. The door of the house was half open, and they heard the owner, an old man, scolding a servant for having thrown away a match without using both ends. After enjoying the dispute for a few moments, they presented themselves to the old gentleman and stated the object of their visit, though from what they had just witnessed, they had little hope of success.

The supposed miser, however, no sooner understood their business than he stepped into a closet, from which he brought a bag, and counted out a large amount of money. The collectors were astonished, and told the man that they had heard the quarrel with the servant.

"Gentlemen," he said, "you are surprised at a very small matter. I keep my house and save money in my own way. With regard to benevolent donations, you can always expect the most from people who take good care of their own money."

When he had finished, he showed them to the door and closed it behind him, not thinking any more about the large amount of money he had given away than the match that had been thrown away.

THE VALUES OF LIFE

A man was surprised that a very talented friend of his could be content with a moderate income.

"I have enough," was the friend's reply. "I don't have enough *time* to make money. Life is not long enough for a man to get rich, and do his duty to his fellowmen at the same time."

—*Spurgeon*

WHAT SHALL WE DO WITH HIM?

A king's guards came running up to him and told him that a robber had entered the castle and had been caught. The king ordered the robber brought before him.

"Well," said the king, "I really don't know what we can do with the rascal. If we put his eyes out, he won't be able to see. If we cut his hands off, he won't be able to work. If we cut off his feet he won't be able to walk. Take him to the kitchen and give him something to eat while we consider what is to be done with him."

After the man had eaten his fill he was again brought before the king. "I really don't see what good it would do us keeping this man here any longer," said the king. "Let him go." And after this gentle reproof from the king, the man was released.

WE RAN FOR OUR LIVES

Down in New Zealand we once had a very destructive flood. In that flood twenty-two white men were drowned. They were working on a railway line that was being constructed. There were a large number of young natives working on the same line. Not one lost his life. At the inquest that was held, one of our young natives was asked if he could give a reason why no natives had lost their lives while so many white men had suffered.

He said, "Yes. The white men ran for their money. We ran for our lives."

—*Matthew Cowley*

FOR THEM

Before you bid, for Christmas' sake,
Your guests to sit at meat,
Oh please to save a little cake
For them that have no treat.

Before you go down party-dressed
In silver gown or gold,
Oh please to send a little vest
To them that still go cold.

Before you give your girl and boy
Gay gifts to be undone,
Oh please to spare a little toy
To them that will have none.

Before you gather round the tree
To dance the day about,
Oh please to give a little glee
To them that go without.
—*Eleanor Farjeon*

THE HONEST EMPLOYER

God's an honest employer.
He's promised to pay.
But He'll double the blessings
That you give away.
—*Richard Devon Walker*

THERE IS NO TRUE ALMS WHICH THE HAND CAN HOLD

There is no true alms which the hand can hold;
He gives nothing but worthless gold
Who gives from a sense of duty;
But he who gives but a slender mite,
And gives to that which is out of sight,
That thread of the all-sustaining Beauty
Which runs through all and doth all unite,—
The hand cannot clasp the whole of his alms,
The heart outstretches its eager palms,
For a god goes with it and makes it store
To the soul that was starving in darkness before.
—*James Russell Lowell*

Obedience and Temptation

THE BOY WHO KEPT OUT WELLINGTON

An English farmer was one day at work in his fields, when he saw a party of hunters riding around his farm. He had one field that he was especially anxious that they should not ride over, since the crop could be very badly injured by the trampling of the horses.

So he sent one of his farmhands to shut the gate and watch it and on no account to let it be opened. The boy went as he was asked, but was scarcely at his post before the hunters came up, ordering the gate to be opened.

This the boy refused to do, stating the orders he had received and his determination not to disobey them. Threats and bribes were offered in vain. One after another came forward as spokesman, but all with the same result. The boy remained immovable in the determination not to open the gate.

After awhile one of the men advanced and said, in commanding tones, "My boy, do you know me? I am the Duke of Wellington. I'm not used to being disobeyed and I command you to open that gate so that I and my friends can pass through."

The boy lifted his hat and stood before the man who all England delighted to honor, and answered firmly, "I am sure the Duke of Wellington would not wish me to disobey orders. I must keep this gate shut and not allow anyone to go through it without my master's permission."

Greatly pleased, the sturdy old warrior lifted his own hat and said, "I honor the man or boy who can be neither bribed nor frightened into doing wrong. With an army of such soldiers I could not only conquer the French, but the world."

THE BRIDGE

A man lived in a cottage by a railroad bridge. It was his job to make sure that when a train crossed the bridge, the track over the bridge was tightly secured. To do this he had to, while the train was passing over the bridge, pull tightly on a lever that made doubly sure the track was locked. One day as a train approached, and as the man prepared to hold the lever tight, he noticed his small son playing on the bridge. He was terrified. He knew there was not enough time for his son to return to land. Because the train was just a few seconds from the boy, the man yelled, "Lie down!" The train passed safely over the bridge and disappeared around a bend. The father rushed out onto the bridge, expecting to find the corpse of his son, but was overjoyed to find that the boy had at once obeyed his order. He had lain down and the whole train had passed over without injuring him.

THE DEVIL AND THE HAM

A man had a smokehouse full of hams, and he had decided to give a ham to some poor person. When he went in, he picked out a nice large ham, and an evil spirit spoke to him: "Now that's a big ham. You don't need to give that person such a large ham. Give him a little one."

But the man answered quickly, "Shut up, Mr. Devil, or I'll give him two hams." The man had no more trouble after that.

FREE AS THE BIRDS

For twelve years of my life, after my father's death, I was free as the birds that fly in the air! There was no restraint further than the counsel from my mother. I took no active part in the Church. I was just as free as nonmembers of the Church feel that they are free.... I am sorry, oh how sorry! that there was no restraint or responsibility placed upon me, that I was not actively engaged in Church work during those twelve years.

—*J. Golden Kimball*

GOD FIRST

"Well, sir," said Mr. Sanderson, looking up from his books, "what do you want with me?"

"I want very much to get a job," was the quick answer of the boy, whose name was Willie Thompson.

"A job? What makes you think I have any work?"

"I read your advertisement in the paper."

"So you read the paper, do you? Well, do you answer the description I gave?"

"I don't know, sir. I thought perhaps you would be willing to try me and see."

"Well now, that's fair. What can you do?"

Willie hesitated a minute. There were a good many things he thought he could do. He didn't see how he could get them all into a short answer. At last he said, "I can do what I am told."

"Can you indeed? Now, if you are entirely sure of that, you are a very unusual boy."

"Well, I mean," said Willie, with his cheeks getting red, "that I can try to do it. I suppose a gentleman would not give me things to do that he knew I couldn't do."

"But suppose I should hire you, and the next morning I should tell you to go to my store, and roll down the hill at the back door twenty-five times. What then?"

"Why," said Willie, and he couldn't help laughing. "I'm sure I could do that, and I would go at it as fast as I could."

"But what would you think of me for giving you such work at that?" said Mr. Sanderson.

"I'd think you were a very silly man, but that wouldn't stop me from doing the work as fast as possible."

"Well, suppose I should tell you to go to the shop next door and watch your chance and steal the nicest looking codfish you saw, and run back with it and put it on my counter. What then?"

"I couldn't do that, sir," answered Willie.

"Why not? You told me you could do what you were told to do."

"So I can. But I had my orders about that a good while ago. 'Thou shalt not steal' is one of my orders. I have to follow that."

"Ah, ha, then! My orders come next to those, do they?"

"Yes, sir. Always."

Willie's voice was as firm as before, but he began to think Mr. Sanderson must be a wicked man, and it would be just as well not to work for

him. But just at this point the gentleman held out his hand.

"We'll shake hands on that, my boy," he said. "And we'll try each other for two weeks, if you say so. I want a boy who always puts God's orders first."

HIS BOSS AND HIS GOD

The president of a large and powerful company ordered one of his employees to do an illegal and immoral job for him. The employee told him that he didn't dare.

"What are you afraid of?" asked the boss. "I'll protect you."

"Will you give me a written promise to that effect?" asked the employee.

"Gladly," said his boss.

The employee quickly went out and shortly returned with a document ready for the boss's signature. The employer read: "I, _____, call upon God to visit me with damnation instead of my employee who is about to commit a sin at my order."

The employer dropped the paper. "Never mind," he said. "I'm sorry. I should have known better."

INTELLIGENT OBEDIENCE

It's possible to keep the law of obedience perfectly—to learn how to listen to counsel, not blindly but intelligently. I had a man who taught me that lesson a few years ago. He was a candidate in a political party, and there came out a rather strong statement from the editorial page of the *Deseret News*—put on the front page where everybody could see it. It was a serious blow to the party of which he was a member, and when I met him on the street a little while later I said, "Did you read the editorial?" (I knew he couldn't have missed it.)

He said, "Yes, I read it and immediately I said to myself, 'Well, I know what the brethren are counseling. I shall do what they have counseled.' But," he added to me, "I didn't feel right in my heart about it. I was quarreling within myself. It took a whole night on my knees praying before I could feel right in accepting the counsel that has been given."

President Brigham Young said, "The greatest

fear I have is that the members of the Church will accept what we say without praying about it and then getting the witness in their heart that what we say is the will of the Lord." That puts upon every individual the responsibility of getting the witness in order that he can intelligently obey the counsel that comes from the authorities of the Church.

—*Harold B. Lee*

KEEPING THE FLOOR CLEAN

On a certain occasion Lord Derby had some workmen in one of his mansions for the purpose of painting and decorating the house. The floor of the central hall was being painted, and a tall and powerfully built young man was at work on one of the walls when Lord Derby came in and, giving orders that a number of slippers were to be placed on the doormat, requested the young man to see that anyone coming in should put on a pair of these slippers before crossing the passage. And he added, "If anyone refuses to do it, you must take him by the shoulders and throw him out."

A short time later a hunting party passed by, and the Duke of Wellington, with his boots covered with mud, opened the door and hurried into the hall. Seeing this, the young man immediately jumped off the ladder on which he was painting and, seizing the intruder by the shoulder, pushed him out of the house. The painter didn't know the duke, and had no idea as to the identity of the person he had so uncere-moniously assisted out of the house.

Shortly afterwards Lord Derby heard of the event, and called all of the household and the men at work into his study and demanded to know who had treated the Duke of Wellington in such an impertinent manner. Imagining that he would be immediately fired, the painter came forward and, in a trembling voice, said, "It was I, sir."

"And why did you do such a thing?" asked Lord Derby.

"You told me to, sir," replied the painter, much to the amazement of all present.

Hearing this, Lord Derby at once turned, and smiling, said, "You were quite right to obey orders."

LOOK OUT

A man went to steal corn from his neighbor's field. He took his little boy with him to keep a lookout, so that he could warn him if anyone should come. Before beginning, the man looked all around, first one way and then the other. And not seeing anyone, he was just about to fill his bag when the son cried out, "Father, there's one way you haven't looked yet!" The father supposed that someone was coming, and asked his son which way he meant. His son answered, "You forgot to look up!"

LOYALTY

A king once commanded a good man to be brought before him in order that he should be forced to deny Christianity and offer a sacrifice to the king's idols. But the man only answered firmly, "My lord, the king, that is something I can never do."

Filled with astonishment and indignation, the king exclaimed, "Are you ignorant of the fact that your life is wholly in my power, that a wink from me would be your death warrant?"

"I am perfectly aware of that," replied the man, "but permit me to lay a simple case before you, and ask your judgment concerning it before my sentence is passed. Suppose one of your truest and most loyal servants should fall into the power of your enemies, who should try to force him to become untrue to you, and failing in their efforts, the servant remained firm and true in his allegiance. Suppose they should strip him of his clothing, and drive him away in shame and disgrace. Tell me, my king, would you not, when he came to you, clothe him richly and give him honor for the shame he had borne?"

"Certainly I would," answered the king, "but what has all this to do with you and me?"

"Only this," replied the good man calmly, "that while you indeed have power to strip me of this poor robe of mortality and send me from the castle in shame and disgrace, I have a greater king who will clothe me in immortal raiment. Shall I, then, for the sake of this poor rag, desert and deny Him?"

The heathen king replied in few words, "Go, your life is yours."

MY LIFE'S BUSINESS

An old man was asked if he did not rejoice that his time was near when he would be called home. He replied, "I have no wish about it. I have nothing to do with death. My business is to live as long as I can—as well as I can—and serve my Master as faithfully as I can, until He shall think proper to call me home."

THE OBSTINATE CITIZENS OF OUDENARDE

Some two centuries ago, the town council of Oudenarde, in Flanders, issued an order that no one was to go into the street after 8:00 P.M., without carrying a lantern. The citizens grumbled, yet none of them dared to disobey the law. But after a general consultation they one and all agreed to carry a lantern, but without putting a candle in it.

Then the council gave orders that every person should carry a candle in his lantern. Whereupon the citizens showed their respect for the law by carrying a candle in it, but not lighting it.

This compelled the council to decree for the third time that each person should carry a lantern containing a lighted candle. The citizens at once submitted to the new order, but carried their lanterns with the lighted candles under their cloaks.

The gentlemen of the council shook their heads in indignation, and immediately ordered that each lantern with its lighted candle was to be carried free and exposed to view. That stopped the little game of those obstinate citizens of Oudenarde.

OUT WITH GENTLEMEN

A president of a certain stake in our Church buys and sells cattle and sheep. He goes east very often to sell. He has a son that he sometimes takes to Chicago with him. This particular son, besides having a mind of his own, has a sense of humor—I mean, he is blessed with a comeback. Well, we're talking now about a certain trip the father made when he took this young man with him. At one time the cattle salesman was called unexpectedly to another town, and the boy was left alone in Chicago in the care of the men who usually bought his father's cattle. Now, part of the program in going east to sell is the entertainment of the buyers. These buyers, knowing the shipper was called away, were doubly determined to spare no means in giving the boy a royal reception. They must take him to the most elite clubhouse in the city. The young man was to receive club hospitality and all the trimmings, and they proceeded accordingly.

The first step towards up-to-date hospitality in a place like he was ushered into is the cocktail bar. It's a place where you are served a cocktail before the meal, and it isn't a fruit cocktail. They had already offered the lad cigarettes, and he had refused. Now came the drink. It was offered him on a shining silver tray. It beckoned him on with all the enticement in the world. As it was offered to him, the boy shook his head. The buyer leading the party, with a mixture of surprise and disgust, made up his mind to put this sissy from Mormondom in his place. Others huddled around, and it was really, in a small way, a fine place to make a grandstand play at the expense of the lad from the West. With a sarcastic grin and a determination to humiliate, he shot out at the boy, "The telephone is right there—would you like to call your mother long distance and ask her if she'd give her consent for you to drink with us?"

Well, that was enough to take the starch out of some fellows. But not this lad. Looking his smart-aleck host steadily in the eye, under full control, he gently countered with, "My mother thinks that tonight I'm out with gentlemen."

—*Marvin O. Ashton*

THE PARABLE OF THE UNWISE BEE

A wild bee from the neighboring hills once flew into the room; and at intervals during an hour or more I caught the pleasing hum of its flight. The little creature realized that it was a prisoner, yet all its efforts to find the exit through the partly opened casement failed. When ready to close up the room and leave, I drew the window wide, and tried at first to guide and then to drive the bee to liberty and safety, knowing well that if left in the room it would die as other insects there entrapped had perished in the dry atmosphere of the enclosure. The more I tried to drive it out, the more determinedly did it oppose and resist my efforts. Its peaceful hum developed into an angry roar, its darting flight became hostile and threatening.

Then it caught me off my guard and stung my hand—the hand that would have guided it to freedom. At last it alighted on a pendant attached to the ceiling beyond my reach of help or injury. The sharp pain of its unkind sting aroused in me rather pity than anger. I knew the inevitable penalty of its mistaken opposition and defiance, and I had to leave the creature to its fate. Three days later I returned to the room and found the dried, lifeless body of the bee on the writing table. It had paid for its stubbornness with its life.

To the bee's short-sightedness and selfish misunderstanding I was a foe, a persistent persecutor, a mortal enemy bent on its destruction, while in truth, I was its friend, offering it ransom of the life it had put in forfeit through its own error, striving to redeem it, in spite of itself, from the prisonhouse of death and restore it to the outer air of liberty.

—*James E. Talmage*

POUNDING ON THE DEVIL'S DOOR

A priesthood leader explained, "So many members rationalize their temptations by saying that the devil is out to get them. The truth is that so many people are pounding on the devil's door that he's too busy entertaining visitors to mail out invitations."

THE SAME OLD ROCKS

President Brigham Young was making one of his tours and arrived at a town in one of the southern counties. He had intended to stop there and speak to the people, but as he drove along the streets entering town, he noticed the unclean condition of the surroundings. He drove direct to the bishop's home, stopped his team and said to the bishop, who stood in front of his residence awaiting the arrival of the President: "Why, Bishop, I see the same old rocks upon the streets; I see the same old dirty surroundings; I see the same old mud puddles before the tithing office and your public buildings, just as they were when I was last here; and inasmuch as I called attention to these defects when I was here before, and it has had no effect upon the people whatever, I do not think it necessary for me to stop this time. Goodbye, Bishop. Tell the people when they attend to

these things and rectify them, I will stop next time."

—*Reed Smoot*

TEMPTATIONED

Little Herbert had been forbidden to go out of the yard. One day he found the gate open, and after hesitating a few moments, shut and fastened it. At night he told of it. "Papa, somebody left that gate wide open today, and it temptationed me to go out into the lot; but I asked the Lord to help me and He did, so I did not go, but just shut the gate up so tight I could not open it again."

THE TWO MEN INSIDE

An old Indian once asked a white man to give him some grain. The man gave him a small sack full.

The next day he came back and asked for the white man. "I found a dollar among the grain," he said.

"Why don't you keep it?" asked a bystander.

"I've got a good man and a bad man here," said the Indian, pointing to his breast, "and the good man said, 'It is not mine; give it back to the owner.' The bad man said, 'Never mind; you got it, and it is your own now.' The good man said, 'No, no, you must not keep it.' So I didn't know what to do and I tried to go to sleep, but the good and the bad men kept talking all night, and troubling me, and now I bring the money back so they can stop fighting and I can feel good."

WANTING TO BE FREE

I shall tell you a story about a horse I once owned and had great pleasure in training. He had a good disposition, a clean, well-rounded eye, was well-proportioned and, all in all, a choice equine possession. Under the saddle he was as willing, responsive, and cooperative as a horse could be. I liked the way he would go up to something of which he was afraid. He had confidence that if he would do as I bade him he would not be injured.

But Dandy resented restraint. He was ill-contented when tied and would nibble at the tie-rope until he was free. He would not run away, he just wanted to be free. Thinking other horses felt the same, he would proceed to untie their ropes. He hated to be confined in the pasture, and if he could find a place in the fence where there was only smooth wire, he would paw the wire carefully with his feet until he could step over to freedom. More than once my neighbors were kind enough to put him back in the field. He even learned to push open the gate. Though his depredations were provoking and sometimes expensive, I admired his intelligence and ingenuity.

But his curiosity and desire to explore the neighborhood led him and me into trouble. Once on the highway he was hit by an automobile, resulting in a demolished machine, injury to the horse, and slight, though not serious, injury to the driver.

Recovering from that, and still impelled with a feeling of wanderlust, he inspected the fence throughout the entire boundary. He even found the gates wired. So, for awhile we thought we had Dandy secure in the pasture.

One day, however, somebody left the gate unwired. Detecting this, Dandy unlatched it and took another horse, his companion, with him, and together they visited the neighbor's field. They went to an old house used for storage. Dandy's curiosity prompted him to push open the door. Just as he had surmised, there was a sack of grain. What a find! Yes, and what a tragedy. The grain was bait for rodents! In a few minutes Dandy and the other horse were in spasmodic pain, and shortly afterwards both were dead.

How like Dandy are many of our youth! They are not bad; they do not even intend to do wrong, but they are impulsive, full of life, full of curiosity, and long to do something. They, too, are restive under restraint, but if they are kept busy, guided carefully and rightly, they prove to be responsive and capable; but if left to wander unguided, they all too frequently violate principles of right which often lead to snares of evil, disaster, and even death.

—*David O. McKay*

WHAT MOTHER WANTS

A small boy was carrying a large bag in which was something that his mother wanted delivered to a neighbor. As he walked down the street a man approached him and asked, "What do you have in that bag, son?"

The boy replied loyally, "My mother would not have put it in this bag if she had wanted it known."

WHAT SORT OF WEATHER

"What sort of weather will we have today?" asked a traveler of an old man.

"Whatever weather I like," was the reply.

"Whatever weather you like? How can that be?"

"Because it will be what God pleases, and what He pleases, I like."

AS GOD WILL

Pain's furnace heat within me quivers,
God's breath upon the flame doth blow,
And every part within me shivers
And quivers in the fiery glow.
Yet say I, trusting: "As God will,"
And in His hottest fires hold still.

He kindles for my profit purely
Affliction's glowing, fiery brand;
And every blow He deals me, surely,
Is given by a master hand.
So say I, hoping: "As God will,"
And in His hottest fires hold still.

Why should I murmur, for thus the sorrow
Only longer-lived would be.
Peace may come—yes, will—tomorrow,
When God has done His work in me.
So say I, praying: "As God will,"
And in His hottest fires hold still.

—*Author Unknown*

BE STRONG

Be strong!
We are not here to play, to dream, to drift;
We have hard work to do, and loads to lift;
Shun not the struggle—face it; 'tis God's gift.

Be strong!
Say not, "The days are evil. Who's to blame?"
And fold the hands and acquiesce—oh shame!
Stand up, speak out, and bravely, in God's name.

Be strong!
It matters not how deep intrenched the wrong,
How hard the battle goes, the day how long;
Faint not—fight on! Tomorrow comes the song.
                                                    —*Malthie Davenport Babcock*

DON'T TRY IT

Playing with temptation,
Saying that you're strong and firm
Is like the fish who says
He'll dodge the hook, but get the worm.
                                                    —*Richard Devon Walker*

EVENSONG

The embers of the day are red
Beyond the murky hill.
The kitchen smokes; the bed
In the darkling house is spread:
The great sky darkens overhead,
And the great woods are shrill.
So far have I been led,
Lord, by Thy will:
So far I have followed, Lord, and wondered still.
The breeze from the embalmed land
Blows sudden towards the shore,
And claps my cottage door.
I hear the signal, Lord—I understand.
The night at Thy command
Comes. I will eat and sleep and will not
    question more.
                                                    —*Robert Louis Stevenson*

GIVE ME YOUR WHOLE HEART

Give me your whole heart,
Love and adore me,
Worship me always,
Bow to me only,
And you shall find me:
This is my promise
Who love you dearly.
Lay down all duties
In me, your refuge.
Fear no longer,
For I will save you
From sin and from bondage.
                                                    —From *"The Bhagavad Gita"*

GOD'S PLAN

One small life in God's great plan,
How futile it seems as the ages roll,
Do what it may, or strive how it can,
To alter the sweep of the infinite whole!
A single stitch in an endless web,
A drop in the ocean's flow and ebb!
But the pattern is rent where the stitch is lost,
Or marred where the tangled threads have
    crossed;
And each life that fails of its true intent
Mars the perfect plan that its Maker meant.
                                                    —*Susan Coolidge*
                                                    From *"Commonplace"*

HE LIVED A LIFE

What was his creed?
I do not know his creed, I only know
That here below, he walked the common road
And lifted many a load, lightened the task,
Brightened the day for others toiling on a
    weary way:
This, his only meed; I do not know his creed.
What was his creed? I never heard him speak
Of visions rapturous, of Alpine peak,
Of doctrine, dogma, new or old;
But this I know, he was forever bold
To stand alone, to face the challenge of each day,
And live the truth, so far as he could see—
The truth that evermore makes free.

His creed? I care not what his creed;
Enough that never yielded he to greed—
But served a brother in his daily need;
Plucked many a thorn and planted many a flower;
Glorified the service of each hour;
Had faith in God, himself, and fellow-men;—
Perchance he never thought in terms of creed,
I only know he lived a life, in deed!
                                                    —*H. N. Fifer*

HONORS

What though unmarked the happy workman toil,
And break unthanked of man the stubborn clod?
It is enough, for sacred is the soil,
Dear are the hills of God.

Far better in its place the lowliest bird
Should sing aright to Him the lowliest song,

Than that a seraph strayed should take the word
And sing His glory wrong.

—Jean Ingelow

———————

SINGLENESS OF HEART

Let us then labor for an inward stillness,
An inward stillness and an inward healing,
That perfect silence where the lips and heart
Are still, and we no longer entertain
Our own imperfect thought and vain opinions,
But God alone speaks in us, and we wait
In singleness of heart, that we may know
His will, and in the silence of our spirits,
That we may do His will, and do that only!

—Henry Wadsworth Longfellow

———————

THUS SPEAKETH CHRIST OUR LORD

Ye call Me Master and obey Me not,
Ye call Me Light and see Me not,
Ye call Me wise and follow Me not,
Ye call Me eternal and seek me not,
Ye call Me gracious and trust me not,
Ye call Me noble and serve Me not,
Ye call Me just and fear Me not;
If I condemn you, blame Me not.

—Author Unknown

———————

THE WISE SEER WITHIN

I will be
Light-hearted as a bird, and live with God.
I find Him in the bottom of my heart,
I hear continually His voice therein;
The little needle always knows the North,
The little bird remembereth his note,
And this wise Seer within me never errs.
I never taught it what it teaches me;
I only follow, when I act aright.

—Ralph Waldo Emerson

———————

Prayer and Music

ASK HIM

The old woman knelt in prayer with her home teachers on their monthly visit. The senior home teacher, a sincere but verbose elder, began to pray. After several minutes of "eloquent" introduction and supplication, in which the attributes of God were being stated at great length, the old woman leaned over and said, "Ask Him for something."

BENJAMIN FRANKLIN'S PROPOSAL

While the important question of the representation of the American States in the senate was the subject of debate, and the states were almost equally divided upon it, Dr. Franklin moved that prayers should be attended in the convention every morning, and in support of his motion, thus addressed the president:

"Mr. President: The small progress we have made after four or five weeks of close attendance and continual reasonings with each other, our different sentiments on almost every question, several of the last producing as many noes as ayes, is, methinks, a melancholy proof of the imperfection of the human understanding. We indeed seem to feel our own want of political wisdom, since we have been running all about in search of it. We have gone back to ancient history for models of government, and examined the different forms of republics, which, having been originally formed with the seeds of their own dissolution, now no longer exist; and we have viewed modern states all around Europe, but find none of their constitutions suitable to our circumstances. In this situation of this assembly, groping, as it were, in the dark, to find political truth, and scarcely able to distinguish it when presented to us, how has it happened, sir, that we have not hitherto once thought of humbly applying to the Father of lights to illuminate our understandings? In the beginning of the contest with Great Britain, and when we were sensible of danger, we had daily prayers in this room for Divine protection. Our prayers, sir, were heard, and they were graciously answered. All of us who were engaged in the struggle must have observed frequent instances of a superintending Providence in our favor. To that kind Providence we owe this happy opportunity of consulting in peace on the means of establishing our future national felicity. And have we now forgotten that powerful Friend? or do we imagine we no longer need His assistance? I have lived, sir, a long time, and the longer I live, the more convincing proofs I see of this truth—that God governs in the affairs of men. And if a sparrow cannot fall to the ground without His notice, is it probable that an empire can rise without His aid? We have been assured, sir, in the sacred writings, that 'except the Lord build the house, they labor in vain that build it.' I firmly believe this; and I also believe, that without this concurring aid, we shall succeed in this political building no better than the builders of Babel; we shall be divided by our little partial local interests, our projects will be confounded, and we ourselves shall become a reproach and a by-word to future ages. And what is worse, mankind may hereafter, from this unfortunate instance, despair of establishing governments by human wisdom, and leave it to chance, war, or conquest. I therefore beg leave to move, that henceforth prayers, imploring the assistance of heaven, and its blessings on our deliberations, be held in this assembly every morning before we proceed to business; and that one or more of the clergy of this city be requested to officiate in that service."

DIDN'T PRAY ENOUGH

One night a strong wind began to blow, shaking the houses. A little boy, hearing the wind and feeling the house shake, awoke and said, "Mamma, can I get up and pray?"

The mother said, "Of course." The little boy got up, knelt by his bed and asked his mother to tell him what to say. She told him to ask the Lord not to let the house blow down, nor the barn, nor the granary. The little boy did as his mother suggested.

Early the next morning the boy got up and went outside to see if his prayer had been answered. The house, the granary, and the barn were all fine. However, in the distance he could see some other people's houses and one of them had been blown over.

"Oh Mamma," he said as he ran indoors, "why didn't you tell me to pray for the other houses not to blow over, too?"

EXCHANGING KINGS FOR GOD

John Mason had served as counselor to four kings of England. He had had a part in most of the important transactions of the state for thirty years. In the evening of his life he declared, "If I were to live again, I would exchange the court for retirement, and the whole life I have lived for one hour's enjoyment of God in prayer. All things now forsake me, except my God and my prayers."

FASTING AND PRAYER

I have a friend down in Honolulu. He was called one day to the hospital by one of our native sisters who had a child there with polio. She said, "Bishop, hurry up to the hospital and give my child a blessing." That was one morning. He never showed up all day. The next afternoon he went up, and she started giving him a tongue lashing. "You, my bishop, your own boss. I asked you to come and bless my child seriously ill, and you didn't show up."

He waited until she had finished and then he said, "When I hung up the receiver yesterday I started to fast. I've been fasting and praying. Now I'm ready." That was early in the afternoon. He blessed the child. The child went home that evening, released from the hospital. "This kind cometh not out save by fasting and prayer."

—*Matthew Cowley*

GOD'S WAY OF ANSWERING PRAYERS

The nestling eaglet looks up to the majestic flight of the soaring eagle through heaven, and says, "Oh that I could soar as bravely! Teach me, teach me to fly!" And, as if in answer to the wish, the parent bird descends and tears the soft nest in pieces, forcing the eaglets to fall into the sweeping winds. And though to the young bird it may seem almost cruel, yet it is just what it longed for—this is teaching it to fly!

—*Wadsworth*

A GOOD REASON FOR PRAYING

A little girl about four years old was asked, "Why do you pray to God?"

She answered, "Because I know He hears me, and I love to pray to Him."

"But how do you know He hears you?"

She put her little hand to her heart, and said, "I know He does, because there is something *here* that tells me so."

HANG ON

When Tom was six years old he went into the forest one afternoon to meet the hired man, who was coming home with a load of wood. The man placed Tom on the top of the load and drove homeward. Just before reaching the farm the team went pretty briskly down a steep hill. When Tommy entered the house his mother said:

"Tommy, my dear, weren't you frightened when the horses were trotting so fast down Crow Hill?"

"Yes, mother, a little," replied Tom, "but I asked the Lord to help me, and hung on like a beaver."

HE HEARD MY PRAYER

When I was in Paris, France, about thirty years ago, I had a dream that troubled me very much, in which I saw my first wife...lying sick at the point of death. And it so affected me that I awoke, being troubled in my feelings. I fell asleep again, and again the same scene presented itself to me when I again awoke and experienced the same feeling of sorrow, and after some time slept again, and it was repeated a third time. I knew then that my wife was very sick, lying at the point of death.

I got up and fervently prayed the Lord to spare her life until at least I should have another opportunity of meeting her in the flesh. *He heard my prayer.* I took a note of the circumstance at the time, and learned afterward that such had been the case exactly as it had been shown to me. On the following morning I remember meeting a gentleman who was a Protestant minister, and he observed that my countenance looked sorrowful, and then inquired the cause. I told him that my wife was lying at the point of death, and he asked me if I had received a letter. I told him how it had been shown to me. But, I said, I got up and prayed the Lord to spare her life, and I feel consoled in *knowing* that she will be healed.

—John Taylor

HOLD FAST BY THE ROPE

When I first amused myself with going out to sea, when the winds arose and the waves became a little rough I found it difficult to keep my legs on the deck, for I tumbled and tossed about like a porpoise on the water. At last I caught hold of a rope that was floating about, and then I was enabled to stand upright. So when in prayer a multitude of troublous thoughts invade your peace, or when the winds and waves of temptation arise, look out for the rope, lay hold of it, and stay yourself on the faithfulness of God in His covenant with His people and in His promises. Hold fast by that rope, and you shall stand.

—Salter

IS HE DONE YET?

A traveling salesman, while visiting a certain city, stopped for the night at the house of a friend of his. That evening the friend called the entire family, the salesman included, together for family prayer. They kneeled, and the friend began to pray. The salesman thought the prayer to be extremely long, but decided that since he was so tired with traveling it was probably shorter than it seemed. Some time later the friend was still praying and the salesman decided that the length of the prayer was not a figment of his imagination. After about an hour of prayer, he became quite impatient and, turning to the man's son who was kneeling next to him, he asked whether his father would be through praying soon.

The boy turned his head and asked, "Has he got to the Jews yet?"

"No," said the salesman.

"Well, then," said the son, bowing his head again, "he's not quite half done yet."

JOHN TAYLOR'S HYMNS

Two men had been full of integrity and devotion to the work of the Lord since the hardships of Nauvoo, and had suffered the drivings and persecutions of the Saints, as well as the hardships of pioneering incident to the early settlement of the West. These men had quarreled over some business affairs, and finally concluded that they would try to get President John Taylor to help them adjust their difficulties.

John Taylor was then the President of the Council of the Twelve Apostles. These brethren pledged their word of honor that they would faithfully abide by whatever decision he might render.

Accordingly, they called on President Taylor. They did not immediately tell him what their trouble was, but explained that they had seriously quarreled and asked him if he would listen to their story and render his decision. President Taylor willingly consented. But he said: "Brethren, before I hear your case, I would like very much to sing one of the songs of Zion for you."

President Taylor was a very capable singer, and interpreted sweetly and with spirit our sacred hymns. He sang one of the hymns to the two brethren.

Seeing its effect, he remarked that he never heard one of the songs of Zion but that he wanted to listen to one more, and so asked them to listen while he sang another. Of course they consented. They both seemed to enjoy it; and, having sung the second song, he remarked that he had heard there is luck in odd numbers and so with their consent he would sing still another, which he did. Then in his jocular way, he remarked, "Now, brethren, I do not want to wear you out, but if you will forgive me, and listen to one more hymn, I promise to stop singing, and will hear your case."

The story goes that when President Taylor had finished the fourth song, the brethren were melted to tears, got up, shook hands, and asked President Taylor to excuse them for having called upon him, and for taking up his time. They then departed without his even knowing what their difficulties were.

—Heber J. Grant

LINCOLN'S PRAYER

It was on the 5th of July, 1863, that I was brought to Washington on a stretcher from the field of Gettysburg. Hearing of my arrival, President Abraham Lincoln came to my room and sat by my bedside. He asked about the great battle, and when I told him of the terrible slaughter the tears streamed from his eyes. I asked him if he had doubted the result. He said "No." Then he continued:

"This may seem strange to you, but a few days ago, when the opposing armies were converging, I felt as never before my utter helplessness in the great crisis that was to come upon the country. I went into my own room and locked the door. Then I knelt down and prayed as I had never prayed before. I told God that He had called me to this position, that I had done all that I could and that the result was now in His hands; that I felt my own weakness and lack of power, and that I knew that if the country was to be saved it was because He so willed it. When I went from my room I felt that there could be no doubt of the issue. The burden seemed to have rolled off my shoulders, my intense anxiety was relieved, and in its place came a great sense of trustfulness, and that was why I did not doubt the results at Gettysburg. And, what is more, Sickles," he continued, "I believe that we may hear at any moment of a great success by Grant, who has been pegging away at Vicksburg for so many months. By tomorrow you will hear that he has won a victory as important to us in the West as Gettysburg is in the East."

Then turning to me, he said, "Sickles, I am in a prophetic mood today and I know that you will get well."

"The doctors do not give me that hope, Mr. President," I said.

But he answered cheerfully, "I know that you will get well, Sickles."

—*General Daniel Sickles*

A LITTLE BOY'S PRAYER

A little boy was upon the operating table, ready to undergo an operation for appendicitis—an orphan boy about eight years of age. It was a rather unusual case, and, by the way, a charity case. As the boy lay there, he looked up at the surgeons—there were several of them present—and addressing the surgeon in charge he said, "Doctor, before you begin to operate, won't you pray for me?"

The surgeon looked at the boy amazed and said, "Why, I can't pray for you."

Then the little fellow turned his eyes from one to the other, asking each if they would pray for him. Each in turn declined. Then the little man said, "If you won't pray for me, won't you please wait while I pray for myself?"

The little fellow got up on the operating table on his knees, folded his hands, and uttered a prayer. He said to the Lord, "Heavenly Father, I am only a little orphan boy, but I am awful sick, and these doctors are going to operate. Will you please help them that they will do it right? And now, Heavenly Father, if you will make me well I will be a good boy. Thank you for making me well." He then turned over and laid on his back and looked up at the doctors and nurses who were all standing around, but he was the only one in the room who could see because the others had tears in their eyes. He said, "Now I am ready."

A few days after that, a man went into the office of the chief surgeon and asked him to tell him the story of the little boy he had operated on a few days before. The surgeon said, "I have operated on a good many little boys."

"Yes, I know, but this was an unusual case—tell me about it."

Then the doctor looked at him for some time and said, "I don't know whether I will tell you or not. I am not sure but that it is too sacred to talk about."

"Please tell me," he replied; "I will treat it as sacred, too." Then the doctor told the story as I have related it, and when he got through the visitor said, "My that was a remarkable experience, wasn't it?"

The doctor said, "Remarkable? That was the most remarkable experience of my whole life. I have operated on hundreds of men, women, and children, and I have known some of them to pray, but never until I stood in the presence of that little boy, have I heard anyone talk to their Heavenly Father face to face."

—*George Albert Smith*

THE POTATO PRAYER

A poor man, who had a large family, worked hard and kept them comfortably though not lavishly supported. One day he broke his leg and could no longer work. Several members of the ward decided to get together and pray for him and his family, who, without his support, was beginning to suffer. Soon after they had gathered at the poor man's house, they were interrupted by a loud knock at the door. A young man was standing there. "Father could not attend this meeting," said the young man, "but he sent his prayers and they're out in the wagon." They were brought in, in the shape of potatoes, beef, pork, and corn. The meeting broke up, and the poor man and his family had no trouble surviving the several weeks he was laid up. They were helped by the "prayers" of their ward members.

THE PRAYER DRILL

One night during the Revolutionary War, near a British camp not far from the Hudson River, a soldier was caught creeping stealthily back to his quarters out of the woods. He was taken before the commanding officer and charged with communicating with the enemy. The poor soldier pleaded that he had only gone into the woods to pray by himself. That was his only defense. The commanding officer seemed to feel no tenderness for the soldier.

"Have you been in the habit, sir, of spending hours in private prayer?" asked the officer sternly.

"Yes, sir."

"Then down on your knees and pray now!" thundered the officer. "You never before had so much need of it."

Expecting immediate death, the soldier knelt and poured out his soul in a prayer that, for aptness and simple expressive eloquence, could have been inspired only by the sincerity of a true Christian.

"You may go," said the officer when he had done. "I believe your story. If you had not gone frequently to drill, you could not have done so well at review."

PRAYING TO WHOM?

A man and his friend were discussing prayer, observing that there were many ways to pray.

"Before I began to understand prayer, during family prayer I would pray to my family. If any strangers were present I would pray to them. When I was alone I would pray to myself. Then I realized what I was doing and in all my prayers began to pray to God. And, strangely enough, my prayers began to be answered."

PROBLEMS AND PRAYERS

I will tell you a circumstance that took place with me upwards of forty years ago. I was living in Canada at the time, and was a traveling elder. I presided over a number of the churches in that district of country. A difficulty existed in a branch of the Church, and steps were taken to have the matter brought before me for settlement.

I thought very seriously about it, and thought it a very insignificant affair, because we ought to soar above such things and walk a higher plane, for we are children of God and should be willing to suffer wrong rather than do wrong; to yield a good deal to our brethren for the sake of peace and quietness, and to secure and promote good feelings among the Saints.

At that time I did not have the experience I now have, and yet I do not know that I could do any better than I did then. Before going to the trial, I bowed before the Lord and sought wisdom from Him to conduct the affair aright, for I had the welfare of the people at heart.

When we had assembled, I opened the meeting with a prayer, and then called upon a number of those present to pray; they did so, and the Spirit of God rested upon us. I could perceive that a great feeling existed in the hearts of those who had come to present their grievances, and I told them to bring forward their case. But they said they had not anything to bring forward.

The feelings and spirit they had been in possession of had left them, the Spirit of God had obliterated these feelings out of their hearts, and they knew it was right for them to forgive one another.

—John Taylor

SHARON'S SECRET

Sharon was doing very well at school. Everybody noticed and her teacher commented on it frequently. Matthew wondered how she did so well, and approached her and asked.

She answered, "I always pray that I may do well in school."

"Do you?" said Matthew. "In that case, I'll pray too."

The next morning, however, Matthew did even worse than ever. Confused, he ran to Sharon and complained, "I prayed, but it didn't help a bit."

"Did you do any studying yesterday?" asked Sharon.

"Study! Study!" exclaimed Matthew. "You mean if I pray I have to study too?"

_____

A SONG IN THE NIGHT

One of the joys of my life centers in the hymns I learned as a child in Sunday School. Never a soloist, I have received great satisfaction in being a humble part of the chorus—in a church choir, in a college glee club, and with the birds outside my kitchen window.

When I am discouraged or worried, I go out to my garden and pick up a watering hose and sing myself into a better mood by humming the tunes or voicing the words of hymns. Sometimes I have to sing loudly to remind myself of the promises of faith and deliverance.

Never was the need more urgent than on a hot night of summer several seasons ago when I went out into the dark while a loved one slept inside, recovering from illness. I was tired and discouraged, and the tension showed in my voice. How fortunate it was, I thought, that everybody within listening distance was away. One neighbor was at the beach, another at the nearby mountains, a third vacationing in another state. The little house on the side street was completely dark, so I supposed this neighbor whom I knew but slightly was away also.

Thus isolated, I started to sing, but my voice broke. Again I tried and had to give it up as a bad job. Finally with almost a yell, I made a third attempt and managed to keep to the tune.

For over an hour I sang, totally undisturbed and feeling completely alone on my little island of depression. Then I went indoors, rested enough by the comfort of the hymns to fall into a deep but troubled sleep.

Next morning there was a knock at the door. There stood the slightly known neighbor, looking wan and pale. She moved shakily into a chair. "I came to thank you for singing those glorious hymns. You will never know how much I needed them."

I told her I had thought I was singing to myself to keep up my own courage. "You strengthened me," she said. "I learned yesterday that I must

have extensive medical care and must move from here to live with my daughter. I was lying in bed fighting the move with all my heart. Now it is all right, and I can do what is necessary."

When she left I reflected anew how we are a part of each other's lives and that it matters indeed how well we bear our own burdens, for unknown to us someone may be needing our strength and courage.

Out of my temporary discouragement and heartache I had sung the hymns of faith, love, and courage, and my neighbor had needed their solace too. I determined to remember that there is a special blessing in facing life with a hymn in the heart.

—Ruth C. Ikerman

_____

TALKING TO GOD

When Dr. Bacchus, the president of Hamilton College, was on his deathbed, the doctor visited him and, after examining the symptoms, left the room without speaking. But as he opened the door to go out, Dr. Bacchus noticed him whisper something to the servant.

"What did the doctor say to you?" asked Dr. Bacchus.

"He said, sir, that you have no more than half an hour to live."

"Is that so? Then take me out of my bed and place me on my knees. Let me spend the time I have left in talking to my God."

His request was complied with, and while praying for those he was leaving behind, he died upon his knees.

—Howes

_____

WHO ARE YOU PRAYING FOR?

A man who had only one prayer which he repeated day after day was asked by his wife to pray at the bedside of their sick child. The man began as he usually did, and soon came to his usual petition for the Jews. As he went on with the time-honored quotation, "Lord, turn again the captivity of Zion," his wife broke in, saying, "Come on, dear. Enough with the Jews. It's our child who's sick." Then clasping her hands she began her own heartfelt pleas for the child.

_____

DE PROFUNDIS

Out of the depths have I cried unto Thee:
"Lord, hear my cry!"
The answer comes in the smile of a friend
Passing nigh.

Out of the depths have I cried unto Thee:
"Lord, still my woe!"
The answer comes in the voice of a friend,
Comforting, low.

Out of the depths have I cried unto Thee:
"Lord, heal my pain!"
The answer comes in the tears of a friend,
Sympathy's rain.

Out of the depths have I cried unto Thee:
"Lord, make me strong!"
The hand of a friend is laid on mine,
Clasping it long.

Out of the depths have I cried unto Thee:
"Clear Thou my doubt!"
The answer comes in the faith of friends,
Encamping about.

—Rollo de Caen

EVENING PRAYER

God of Mercy:
The day with all its choices, good or ill,
Is now beyond recall;
And I am alone with Thee,
To make answer for deed and word and thought.
I cannot play the hypocrite with Thee;
I cannot excuse or justify the blots that stained
    the day;
I cannot lightly laugh at my transgressions now;
For Thou does know me altogether.
But Thou does know the good in me, and not the
    evil only;
Dost see my struggles, mark my resolutions,
Hear my silent prayers in heaven, Thy dwelling
    place.
Thy heart is kind.
There is forgiveness with Thee.
It was for men like me that Jesus died.
For His sake, let me know Thy peace tonight,
And with the morrow make me to be
A new and worthier man.

—Robert Freeman

FOR ALL WHO NEED

For all who watch tonight—by land or sea or air—
O Father, may they know that Thou art with
    them there.

For all who weep tonight, the hearts that
    cannot rest,
Reveal Thy love, that wondrous love which gave
    for us Thy best.

For all who wake tonight, love's tender watch
    doth keep,
Watcher Divine, Thyself draw nigh, Thou who
    dost never sleep.

For all who fear tonight, whatever the dread may
    be,
We ask for them the perfect peace of hearts that
    rest in Thee.

Our own beloved tonight, O Father, keep, and
    where
Our love and succor cannot reach, now bless
    them through our prayer.

And all who pray tonight, Thy wrestling hosts,
    O Lord,
Make Weakness strong, let them prevail
    according to Thy word.

—Author Unknown

JUST WHISTLE A BIT

Just whistle a bit, if the day be dark
And the sky be overcast:
If mute be the voice of the piping lark,
Why, pipe your own small blast.

Just whistle a bit, if the night be drear
And the stars refuse to shine:
And a gleam that mocks the starlight clear
Within you glows benign.

Just whistle a bit, if there's work to do,
With the mind or in the soil.
And your note will turn out a talisman true
To exorcise grim Toil.

It will lighten your burden and make you feel
That there's nothing like work as a sauce for a
    meal.

And with song in your heart and the meal in its
    place,
There'll be joy in your bosom and light in your
    face.

Just whistle a bit, if your heart be sore;
'Tis a wonderful balm for pain.
Just pipe some old melody o'er and o'er
Till it soothes like summer rain.
—Paul Laurence Dunbar

LAUGHING SONG

Sing us something full of laughter;
Tune your harp, and twang the strings
Till your glad voice, chirping after,
Mates the song the robin sings:
Loose your lips and let them flutter
Like the wings of wanton birds,—
Though they naught but laughter utter,
Laugh, and we'll not miss the words.

Sing in ringing tones that mingle
In a melody that flings
Joyous echoes in a jingle
Sweeter than the minstrel sings:
Sing of Winter, Spring or Summer,
Clang of war, or low of herds;
Trill of cricket, roll of drummer—
Laugh, and we'll not miss the words.

Like the lisping laughter glancing
From the meadow brooks and springs,
Or the river's ripples dancing
To the tune the current sings—
Sing of Now, and the Hereafter;
Let your glad song, like the birds',
Overflow with limpid laughter—
Laugh, and we'll not miss the words.
—James Whitcomb Riley

LIBERTY

Days of toil when the bleeding hand
Of the pioneer grew numb,
When the untilled tracts of the barren land
Where the weary ones had come
Could offer nought from a fruitful soil
To stay the strength of the stranger's toil.

Days of pain, when the heart beat low,
And the empty hours went by

Pitiless, with the wail of woe
And the moan of Hunger's cry—
When the trembling hands upraised in prayer
Had only the strength to hold them there.

Days when the voice of hope had fled—
Days when the eyes grown weak
Were folded to, and the tears they shed
Were frost on a frozen cheek—
When the story bent down from the skies and
    gave
A shroud of snow for the Pilgrim's grave.

Days at last when the smiling sun
Glanced down from a summer sky,
And a music rang where the rivers run,
And the waves went laughing by;
And the rose peeped over the mossy bank
While the wild deer stood in the stream and
    drank.

And the birds sang out so loud and good,
In a symphony so clear
And pure and sweet the woodman stood
With his ax upraised to hear,
And to shape the words of the tongue unknown
Into a language all his own:—

"Sing! every bird, today!
Sing for the sky so clear,
And the gracious breath of the atmosphere
Shall waft our cares away.
Sing! sing! for the sunshine free;
Sing through the land from sea to sea;
Lift each voice in the highest key
And sing for Liberty!

Sing for the arms that fling
Their fetters in the dust
And lift their hands in higher trust
Unto the one Great King;
Sing for the patriot heart and hand;
Sing for the country they have planned;
Sing that the world may understand
This is Freedom's land!"
—James Whitcomb Riley

MATINS

These things I do engage to do;
Hourly to keep my doing true
To what my conscience knows,

To send my soul upon its round
Of this day's duty with no sound
Of plaining of my woes;

To live more worthy of their love
Whom I do love all else above—
And fight my rightful foes.

God give me guidance in my ways
To do the things I should;
God give me length and strength of days
To do the things I would.

—*John Finley*

MUSIC

How many of us ever stop to think
Of music as a wondrous magic link
With God; taking sometimes the place of prayer,
When words have failed us 'neath the weight of
    care?
Music, that knows no country, race or creed;
But gives to each according to his need.

—*Author Unknown*

A NEW YEAR PRAYER

Father, I will not ask for wealth or fame,
Though once they would have joyed my carnal
    sense:
I shudder not to bear a hated name,
Wanting all wealth, myself my sole defense.
But give me, Lord, eyes to behold the truth;
A seeing sense that knows the eternal right;
A heart with pity filled, and gentlest ruth;
A manly faith that makes all darkness light:
Give me the power to labor for mankind;
Make me the mouth of such as cannot speak:
Eyes let me be to groping men, and blind;
A conscience to the base; and to the weak
Let me be hands and feet; and to the foolish,
    mind;
And lead still farther on such as Thy kingdom
    seek.

—*Theodore Parker*

OUR BURDEN BEARER

The little sharp vexations
And the briars that cut the feet,
Why not take all to the Helper

Who has never failed us yet?
Tell Him about the heartache,
And tell Him the longings too,
Tell Him the baffled purpose
When we scarce know what to do.
Then, leaving all our weakness
With the One divinely strong,
Forget that we bore the burden
And carry away the song.

—*Phillips Brooks*

PRAYER

Keep me from fretting, Lord, today
About my lightened purse;
An empty soul, an empty mind
Are infinitely worse.
Keep me from dwelling, Lord, I pray,
Upon tomorrow's bread;
But grant my brother's need shall find
I thought of him instead.

—*May Carleton Lord*

A PRAYER

Give me work to do;
Give me health;
Give me joy in simple things.
Give me an eye for beauty,
A tongue for truth,
A heart that loves,
A mind that reasons,
A sympathy that understands;
Give me neither malice nor envy,
But a true kindness
And a noble common sense.
At the close of each day
Give me a book,
And a friend with whom
I can be silent.

—*Author Unknown*

SEEKING GOD

I said, "I will find God," and forth I went
To seek Him in the clearness of the sky,
But He, over me, stood unendurably
Only a pitiless sapphire firmament
Ringing the world—blank splendor; yet intent
Still to find God, "I will go seek," said I,
"His way upon the waters," and drew nigh

An ocean marge weed-strewn and foam-besprent;
And the waves dashed on idle sand and stone,
And very vacant was the long, blue sea;
But in the evening as I sat alone,
My window open to the vanishing day,
Dear God! I could not choose but kneel and pray,
And it sufficed that I was found by Thee.
—Edward Dowden

THESE ARE THE GIFTS I ASK

These are the gifts I ask
Of Thee, Spirit serene:
Strength for the daily task,
Courage to face the road,
Good cheer to help me bear the traveler's load,
And, for the hours of rest that come between,
An inward joy of all things heard and seen.

These are the sins I fain
Would have Thee take away:
Malice and cold disdain,
Hot anger, sullen hate,
Scorn of the lowly, envy of the great,
And discontent that casts a shadow gray
On all the brightness of the common day.
—Henry Van Dyke

TIMES WITHOUT NUMBER HAVE I PRAYED

Times without number have I prayed,
"This only once forgive";
Relapsing, when Thy hand was stayed,
And suffered me to live:—

Yet now the kingdom of Thy peace,
Lord, to my heart restore:
Forgive my vain repentances,
And bid me sin no more.
—Charles Wesley

THE UPPER ROOM

There is a little chamber kept for me
By hands I see not, yet, unseeing, love,
Where I may enter, still, alone and free.

Its open windows look afar and near.
It has the scent of field and piney grove.
The sea's low song drifts in with quiet cheer.

Its walls are hung with gathered memories,
Dear tokens of the scenes and souls I love,
And trophies of remembered victories.

Here the swung door all alien sound debars
And day is peace; and through the dome above
Shine down by night the sympathetic stars.

It is to sweet, familiar! Here I come
From eager toil or fields where virtue strove
When the heart needs the ministries of home.

It is the little secret chamber, Prayer:
Where the spent soul its unspent life may prove.
God opens such for all men, everywhere.
—Charles Poole Cleaves

Pride and Humility

DO AS THE DEAD DO

A young man, about to enter a prestigious career, asked a respected professor of his for some last-minute advice. The professor told him to go to a cemetery and criticize the dead, and after that to flatter them.

The young man was surprised, but did so.

"Well," asked the professor after the young man had returned, "how did the dead take the abuse you gave them?"

"They didn't say a thing," said the young man.

"And how did they handle the flattery?"

"They didn't seem to notice that either," said the young man.

"You do the same," said the professor.

THE ELEGANT CONSTRUCTION

A visitor to a large city was invited by a friend to see a large, elegant building that had been newly constructed. On their way to the building, however, the visitor stopped and walked over to a small park they were passing. He stooped down, cradled a flower in his hands and smelled it. "You have some nice buildings here," he said, "but I see more of God in this flower than in all of the beautiful buildings in the world."

FOLLY OF FASHION

A man who was supposedly an idiot ran about the streets naked, carrying a piece of cloth on his shoulders. When he was asked why he did not dress himself, since he had the materials, he replied, "Because I'm waiting to see what the style will be when fashion finally quits changing."

HOW TO KNOW A GOOSE

"Mother, mother!" cried a young bird, returning hurriedly from its first flight. "I'm so frightened! I've seen such a sight!"

"What have you seen, my son?" asked the mother bird.

"Oh, white creatures! screaming and running, and straining their necks, and holding their heads so high. See, mother, there they go!"

"Geese, my son, merely geese," calmly replied the parent bird. "Through life, child, observe that when you meet anyone who makes a great fuss about himself, and tries to lift his head higher than the rest of the world, you may know at once he is a goose."

THE HUMBLE GOAT

In a mountain pass there is a narrow ledge of rock, only wide enough for the small feet of a goat to walk upon. On each side there is a deep chasm. On this ledge one day two goats met. There was no room for them to pass each other, or to turn around. The one that did so would fall and be dashed to pieces on the rocks below. The goats sensed their danger and cried loudly in distress. Many people heard them but none could give the least help. The goats stood face to face for a long time. At last one knelt and crouched down as close to the ground as he could. The other goat carefully walked over him, and both goats were saved.

HUMBLE KINGS

King Alphonsus would often, like King Benjamin, work in the fields alongside his subjects. When some found fault with this practice, he smiled and said, "Has God given hands to kings in vain?"

I CAN WAIT

It is said that Kepler, the astronomer who discovered the laws which govern the movement of the planets, saw his great labors despised by his contemporaries. Reduced by extreme misery, he was on his deathbed when a friend asked him if he did not suffer intensely in dying thus without seeing his discoveries appreciated.

"My friend," replied Kepler, "God waited five thousand years for one of His creatures to discover the admirable laws which He has given to the stars, and cannot I wait also until justice is done me?"

—*Eugene Bersier*

THE KING AND THE CHILD

King Frederick VI of Denmark, while traveling one day entered a village school and found the children lively and intelligent and quite ready to answer questions.

"Well, youngsters," he said, "what are the names of the greatest kings of Denmark?"

With one accord they cried out, "Canute the Great, Waldemar and Christian IV."

Just then a little girl, to whom the schoolmaster had whispered something, stood up and raised her hand.

"Do you know another?" asked the king.

"Yes, Frederick VI."

"What great act did he perform?"

The girl hung her head and stammered out, "I don't know."

"That's all right, my child," said the king, "I don't know either."

THE MAYOR AND THE FIRE

At a city banquet the mayor was sitting quite near a fireplace. He was very finely and expensively dressed. A man, noticing that the fire was scorching the mayor's clothing, left his place and went up to the mayor and said, "I have something to tell you."

"Is it pleasant or is it disagreeable?" asked the mayor angrily.

The man, annoyed at the tone of voice, answered briefly, "It's disagreeable."

"Very well, then," said the mayor. "Tell me after dinner."

The man, offended, returned to his seat. He noticed sparks fall on the mayor's clothing and burn their way through.

After the banquet the mayor came to the man and asked, "Well, what is it you have to tell me?"

"Merely, sire," said the man, "that you were sitting too close to the fire and your clothes are completely ruined."

A MIRACLE

A young woman embraced the gospel in the north of Ireland a number of years ago. For a long time she had been hungering and thirsting after righteousness. The Lord knew this, and in his mercy he sent an elder to her with glad tidings which filled her soul with unquenchable joy. She was an invalid; she had not been able to use her limbs for years, and in other ways was greatly deformed.

A natural compassion for her filled the bosoms of the Saints. We felt that here was a case on which the Lord ought to surely manifest His power. We would fast and pray in her behalf, that when she was baptized she might be healed. Fast and prayer meetings were held, and the Lord was implored (commanded would be nearer the truth) to heal her. The majority of all present felt that she would be healed, but some doubted. An over-zealous elder assured the young woman that as soon as she came up out of the water, she would be made whole in every way.

The morning of her baptism came. A number of the young lady's friends were invited to witness the ceremony, but more properly speaking, the coming miracle. A carriage was hired, and the young woman was driven to the public baths. There the driver was dismissed, told that his services would no longer be required, as the young lady was going to walk home. The proprietor of the baths was invited to witness the miracle.

A miracle was performed that day, but it was far different than we expected. The young woman was baptized and confirmed, but she was not healed. Something almost bordering on consternation seized some of the elders as they saw their promises fall to the ground unfulfilled.

The young woman looked up, her face beaming with joy, and said: "Brethren, don't feel bad, I have not been healed as you promised me I would be, but I have a stronger testimony than the testimony of healing. The Lord has fulfilled His promise, and has given me the testimony of His Holy Spirit, which bears witness with my spirit that I have done His holy will."

A hack was sent for, and the young woman was taken to her home, while we returned to our homes sadder but wiser men. A few months later, the dear young sister fell asleep in full fellowship of the Church.

"Why was she not healed?" you ask. One of the reasons was that we had gone contrary to the counsels of the Master, who, in revelation given to the Prophet Joseph, commanded the elders not to boast of these things before the world. (See D&C 105:24.) Yet this is what we had done. How could we expect the blessing?

—*William A. Morton*

A NOBLE HOSPITAL

Dom Pedro of Brazil on one occasion wished to build a hospital and, funds being a little low, he hit upon the idea of ennobling any citizen who would contribute a certain sum to the hospital fund. He soon found that half of Rio de Janeiro was anxious to possess a title, and money poured in from every side. When the hospital was finished, the emperor had carved above the gates a Latin phrase which said, "Human Vanity's Gift to Human Misery."

THE PROUD AND JEALOUS

Dionysius, the tyrant, punished a beautiful musician because he could sing better than himself, and the philosopher Plato because he was more skilled at debate.

Canobyses, king of Persia, killed his brother because he was stronger than himself or any of his followers, and Caligula slew his brother because he was better looking than himself.

How often we see this hateful spirit manifested in society. Instead of being jealous or angry because of another's accomplishments, we should rejoice at their progress and success.

PROUD OF HIS ANCESTORS

Voltaire had once taken a box at the opera and was seated in it with some ladies, when the Duke of Lauzun, one of the worst men in the time of Louis XV, arrived and asked for a box. He was respectfully informed that all the boxes were taken.

"That may be," he said, "but I see Voltaire in one. Turn him out."

In those times such things could happen, and Voltaire was turned out. He brought a suit against the duke to recover the price of the box.

"What!" exclaimed the duke's lawyer, "is it Mister Voltaire who dares to sue the Duke of Lauzun, whose great-grandfather was the first to get on the walls of La Rochelle against the Protestants; whose grandfather took twelve cannon from the Dutch at Utrecht; whose father captured two standards from the English at Fontenoy, who—"

"Oh, but excuse me," interrupted Voltaire, "I am not suing the Duke of Lauzun who was first on the walls at La Rochelle, nor against the duke who captured twelve cannon from the Dutch at Utrecht, nor against the duke who captured two standards from the English at Fontenoy. I am suing the Duke of Lauzun who never captured anything in his life but my box at the opera."

STANDING ON ONE LEG

A dancer once said to Socrates, "You can't stand so long on one leg as I can."

"True," replied the philosopher, "but a goose can."

STOOP! STOOP!

Benjamin Franklin was once visiting a friend. "He received me in his study, and at my departure showed me a shorter way out of his house through a narrow passage crossed by a beam overhead. We were talking as we withdrew, when he suddenly cried, 'Stoop! Stoop!' I did not know what he meant until I felt my head hit against the beam. He was a man that never failed to impart instruction; and on this occasion said, 'You are young, and have to go through the world. Stoop as you go through it, and you will miss many hard thumps.' This advice, thus beat into my head, has been of singular service to me, and I have often thought of it when I have seen pride mortified, and men brought low by carrying their heads too high."

THE STUBBORN OTHER FOLK

Colonel Page, who commanded a Pennsylvania regiment in the Civil War, often used to tell laughingly his first experience in marching the raw men who had enlisted. He was given command of a company and, after some preparatory drill, led them down a street in Philadelphia. They marched as well as could be expected for several blocks, when suddenly from the ranks rang out a loud "Halt!"

The men wavered and then came to a full stop.

"Who gave that order?" thundered the enraged captain.

"Potts, sir! Potts!" a dozen voices called out, and every eye turned on Potts, a stout German, a butcher by trade.

"What do you mean, sir, by giving that order?" demanded the captain.

"Well, sir, I've been trying for two blocks to get this company to keep step with me, and they wouldn't do it. So I stopped them to begin all over again."

TYPES OF PRIDE

Diogenes was an ancient cynic who grumbled out some bits of wisdom and went about the streets clothed in rags. Not that he was obliged to do so; he preferred to attract notice in this manner. One day he paid a visit to Plato. He found the philosopher living in a comfortable house, with easy chairs and pleasant pictures around him; and he came in with his feet stained with dust and mud, and exclaimed as he walked upon the beautiful carpets, "Thus I trample on the pride of Plato." The good philosopher paid no attention at first, but repaid the visit, and when he saw the ragged furniture and scanty coverings of the floor of the house in which the other ostentatiously lived, he said, "I see the pride of Diogenes through the holes in his carpet."

WASHINGTON'S POLITENESS

While visiting a small town in New Hampshire, George Washington was approached and saluted by a poor, ragged soldier who had served under him and lost a limb. Washington shook the soldier's hand and gave him a gift of a silver dollar.

One of Washington's attendants expressed scorn that the President of the United States would humble himself by contact with such a poor man. Washington uttered this sharp but merited rebuke:

"Had I allowed him to excel me in politeness, my conscience would upbraid me for such a discourteous act. But now he is my friend and his friendship is more sincere than that of many who flatter me with their attentions."

The officer bit his lip, and his companions smiled among themselves as they moved on in silence.

WELL, YOU'LL DO

At the Centennial Exhibition held in Philadelphia, a certain member of the City Council arrived on the morning of the opening day in elegant attire. With a huge chest which displayed a white vest, a spotless shirt, and a heavy gold watch chain, the newcomer evidently intended to impress everybody with the importance of his civic dignity. Addressing the keeper of the turnstile, who evidently had taken stock of the elaborate "get up" of the official, he remarked, "I'm Councilor Thompson."

Quietly eyeing the pompous man from head to foot, the gatekeeper replied, "Ah, well, you'll do. Pay your dollar and you can come in."

WHEAT AND HUMILITY

A farmer went with his son into a wheat field to see if it was ready for the harvest. "See, father!" exclaimed the boy, "how straight these stems hold up their heads. They must be the best ones. Those than hang their heads down, I am sure, cannot be good for much."

The father plucked a stalk of each kind, and said, "See here, child. This stalk that stood so straight and high is light-headed, the grain in it being shrunken and almost good for nothing, while this that hung its head so modestly is full of the most beautiful grain."

WISDOM AND MODESTY

Aboo Yusuph was chief judge of Bagdad in the reign of the Caliph Hadee. His sense of his own deficiencies often led him to be doubtful about a case while men of less knowledge and more prejudice were decided.

On one occasion, after a very patient investigation of facts, the judge declared that his knowledge was not competent to decide upon the case before him.

"Do you expect," said one of the rude courtiers of the king, who heard the declaration, "that the caliph is to pay you for your ignorance?"

"I do not," was the mild reply. "The caliph pays me, and well, for what I do know. If he were to attempt to pay me for what I do not know, the treasures of his empire would not suffice."

HUMILITY

I know. It is not easy to explain.
Why should there be such agony to bear?
Why should the whole wide world be full of pain?
But then, why should her hair
Be like the sudden sunshine after rain?

Turn cynic if you will. Curse God and die.
You've ample reason for it. There's enough
Of bitterness, God knows, to answer why.
The road of life is rough,
But then, there is the glory of the sky.
—*G. A. Studdert-Kennedy*

OPPORTUNITY

This I beheld, or dreamed it in a dream:—
There spread a cloud of dust along a plain;
And underneath the cloud, or in it, raged
A furious battle, and men yelled, and swords
Shocked upon swords and shields. A prince's banner
Wavered, then staggered backward, hemmed by foes.

A craven hung along the battle's edge,
And thought, "Had I a sword of keener steel—
That blue blade that the king's son bears—but this
Blunt thing!"—he snapped and flung it from his hand.
And lowering crept away and left the field.

Then came the king's son, wounded, sore bestead,

And weaponless, and saw the broken sword,
Hilt-buried in the dry and trodden sand,
And ran and snatched it, and with battle-shout
Lifted afresh he hewed his enemy down,
And saved a great cause that heroic day.
—*Edward R. Sill*

RACE-MEMORY
(BY A DAZED DARWINIAN)

I remember, I remember,
Long before I was born,
The tree-tops where my racial self
Went dancing round at morn.

Green wavering archipelagos,
Great gusty bursts of blue,
In my race-memory I recall
(Or I am told I do).

In that green-turreted Monkeyville
(So I have often heard)
It seemed as if a Blue Baboon
Might soar like a Blue Bird.

Low crawling Fundamentalists
Glared up through the green mist,
I hung upon my tail in heaven
A Firmamentalist.

. . . .

I am too fat to climb a tree,
There are no trees to climb;
Instead, the factory chimneys rise,
Unscaleable, sublime.

The past was bestial ignorance:
But I feel a little funky,
To think I'm further off from heaven
Than when I was a monkey.
—*G. K. Chesterton*

TO SPEAK

To verbalize your sentiments
Loquaciously is grand.
But better is to speak so that
The other'll understand.
—*Richard Devon Walker*

TEACHERS

If in the clutch of things my heart shall lose
Serenity, let me stand still and raise
My eyes to these remembered peaks that gaze
Steadfast when fog-filled valley roads confuse:

If in the toils of selfishness I choose
To dole out service by the rule of days,
Let me recall these lavish garden ways
Where petals fall uncounted in the dews.

Such wisdom is not found in any book,
Such truths are not for pedants to express,
And this is holy ground on which I tread:
I cannot meet a mountain's level look
Without a blush of shame for pettiness,
Nor walk in gardens and not bow my head.

—*Molly Anderson Haley*

———————

Repentance

ACCOMPLICES IN SIN

The father of a family had been in the habit of stealing to support his wife and children. On his deathbed he sent for his lawyer to make out his will. "Write," he said, "the following bequests. First, I leave my soul to the devil." The family began to exclaim that the poor man was delirious. The man replied, "I am not delirious, Lawyer, write: I leave my soul to the devil, that he may carry it to hell, in punishment of the thefts I have committed. Secondly, I leave to the devil the soul of my wife, who encouraged me to steal so that she could indulge her vanity. Thirdly, I leave to the devil the souls of my children, who have been the cause of my thefts." His clergyman, standing by him, exhorted him not to despair, but to have trust in God. But the dying man concluded his will, saying: "Lastly, I leave to the devil the soul of my clergyman, because he always absolved me, without requiring me to make restitution."

—Ardia

A CONSCIENCE AROUSED

The speaker had been speaking on the sins and consequences of dishonesty. A small businessman in the congregation, whose conscience had been aroused, exclaimed to a neighbor on going home, "The speaker needn't have been so hard. There are plenty of dishonest men in this town besides me."

A DAY LOST

It was a noteworthy practice of Vespasian, the Roman Emperor, throughout the course of his whole life, to call himself to account every night for the actions of the past day; and as often as he found he had passed any one day without doing some good, he entered in his diary this note: "I have lost a day."

IT'S TOO LATE NOW

A man was very sick. Not knowing whether he would get well or not, and finally fearing that he would not appear clean before the judgment of God, he contemplated repenting of his sins and bad habits. But he decided not to.

His wife, afraid he would die in his sins, pleaded with him.

"Now, now," he answered her. "If I get better, my friends will only make fun of me. I'll wait until we're sure what's going to happen to me."

Several weeks later the doctor gave up hope of the man's recovering. The man was told he had a very few days to live.

"Please, dear," begged his wife, "renounce your past and turn to God."

"I wish I could," said the man, "but it's too late. I have already been judged and condemned."

LIVEN UP, FATHER

A man who spent most of his time lazing around the house and watching television had his conscience aroused when he heard that his little girl had been asked if her father was living. She had replied, "Not very living."

NOT HER TYPE OF PEOPLE

There were once three sisters who lived together. Two were trying their best to keep the commandments but the third was too interested in pursuing worldly pleasures. One morning she awoke worried because of a dream she had had that night. At breakfast she told it to her sisters:

"I dreamed that I was walking in a city where many others were walking. The atmosphere was full of light, not dazzling but calm, lovely and changeless. The people seemed full of peace and purity. All was beautiful, bright and perfect, and yet the beauty of the place depressed me. I saw that the people were all moving in one direction; and I followed and entered with them into the hall of a large building. It was not built of marble or gold, but of pure consolidated light. Inside was a staircase and many were ascending in white and spotless garments. I also ascended and entered a hall of unspeakable beauty where happy people were dancing to heavenly music. I sank down, overpowered and wretched, and crept into a corner to hide myself, for I felt I had nothing in common with these people. But as I watched, one left the dance and invited me to join them. I suddenly felt angry and answered sharply, 'I will not join your song, for I do not know the tune; I will not join your dance, for I do not know the steps.' He sighed, and with a look of pity returned to the dance. About a minute later, another came and addressed me, and I answered him with the same anger and words. Finally the Master of the dance came and asked me to join the dance and song. Unutterable love seemed to beam from Him upon me, as though it would have melted a heart of stone. I felt it, but my heart grew harder and my voice was bold. I gazed one instant, and replied, 'I will not join your song, for I do not know the tune. I will not join your dance for I do not know the steps.' As I spoke, His countenance changed from one of hope to one of sorrow, and He asked, 'Then what are you doing here?' The floor beneath me then opened and as I was sinking into the earth I woke up.''

Her sisters were shocked and distressed at this dream and implored her to change her ways. The wayward sister, however, only answered, "Don't preach to me. I'll do as I please." She continued in her wayward state until the end of her life.

NOT PREPARED FOR A LONG TRIP

In the seventeenth century, a king died. Soon after his death, a servant of the king came to the jester and said, "Our king is gone."

The jester answered, "And where has he gone?"

"To heaven, I'm sure."

"To heaven! Why, that's impossible!" exclaimed the jester.

"Why so?" asked the servant.

"Because heaven is a long way off, and when the king was going on a long journey he used to spend a great deal of time talking about it and preparing for it. But I never heard the king speak of heaven, or saw him make any preparations for going. He could not possibly have gone there."

PLENTY OF TIME?

A young prince asked his tutor to give him some instruction about preparing for death.

"Plenty of time for that when you are older," said the tutor.

"No," said the child, "I have been to the churchyard and measured the graves, and there are many shorter than I am."

SERVING MEN AND GOD

A courtier who had passed his life in the service of his prince fell dangerously ill. The prince went to visit him, accompanied by his other courtiers. He found him in agony and at the point of death. Touched with the sad spectacle, the prince asked, "Is there anything I can do for you? Ask and I will give it to you."

"Prince," replied the dying man, "I have but one thing to ask of you. Give me a quarter of an hour of life."

"I'm sorry," said the prince, "what you ask is not in my power to give. Ask something else and I'll gladly give it to you."

"What!" said the man, "I have served you for fifty years, and you cannot give me a quarter of an hour of life. If I had served the Lord as faithfully as I have served you He would have given me, not a quarter of an hour of life, but an eternity of happiness."

SOWING OATS TO GET BARLEY

It was planting time and the farmer told his farmhand to sow a certain field with barley. The farmhand went out and sowed the field instead with oats. As the seeds began to grow the farmer noticed that oats, not barley, was springing up.

"Didn't I tell you to sow barley here?" the farmer asked angrily. "Why, then, have you sown oats?"

The farmhand answered, "I sowed oats in the hope that barley would grow."

"That's stupid. Where did you get a foolish idea like that?"

"From you, sir. You're constantly sowing seeds of evil in the field of the world and yet you expect to reap fruits of virtue in the Resurrection. Therefore, I thought I could get barley by sowing oats."

THIS STANDS FOR NOTHING IF I GET BETTER

A man lay dying. His minister visited him and earnestly asked him to be reconciled to a neighbor with whom he had had a long-standing feud. At last the man consented and the neighbor was sent for, and after a brief conversation they shook hands in friendship. But as the neighbor turned to leave, the sick man exclaimed, "But you must remember that if I get better then the whole deal is off."

—*J. C. Antliff*

THREE WORDS

A vicious and ungodly man, when requested to repent, would say that all he needed to do was say three words at his death, and he would be saved. The three words were, "Miserere mei Deus," or "Lord, have mercy upon me." But one day, riding over a bridge, his horse stumbled, and both fell into the river. In the man's death dive the only thing he could say was "Capiat omnia diabolus," or "Horse and man and all to the devil." Three words he had said, but not those he had expected to say. He had been so familiar with the devil all his life that he thought of nothing else at his death. He who travels the way to hell all his life should not expect the end of his journey to be in heaven.

—*T. Stapleton*

THE TWO FAIR FIGHTS

A man once heard some rattling out in his woodpile. He went cautiously to the window, and saw a woman filling her apron with wood, which she quickly carried away. Shortly afterwards he heard the noise a second time, and again saw the woman filling her apron. When she had gone he felt pity for the poverty that had led this woman to steal. By and by he was startled by a crash of falling wood, and, hurrying to the window, saw the poor woman brushing wood dust from her apron. She quickly went away, and soon returned with the second load of wood, which she threw on the pile as if it were cursed. The man's compassion and curiosity were now aroused. He followed her until he discovered where she lived and found out who she was. He then went home, loaded a truck full of wood, and late that night took it to the woman's home where he unloaded it.

The woman, when she arose the next morning and saw the wood, was shocked. A neighbor, who had chanced to see the man bring the wood and dump it, told her what had happened and who the man was. The conscience-stricken woman, realizing it to be the man from whom she had taken the wood, rushed over to his house to thank him and apologize for having taken the wood in the first place.

"Sir," she said, "though my house was dark and cold, though I could hardly bear to see my children shivering, I could not keep the wood. My conscience would not let me."

"Say no more," said the man. "I saw it all. I saw you conquer the devil in two fair fights."

WASHINGTON'S ARGUMENT

When young George Washington was stationed in Alexandria with a regiment under his command, he got into a heated political discussion with a Mr. Payne, who struck Washington and knocked him to the ground. On hearing of the insult given their commander, the regiment, burning for revenge, immediately started for the city. But Washington met them and begged them, by their regard for him, to return peaceably to their barracks. Realizing that he had said some unkind things to Mr. Payne, Washington resolved to make amends, and the next morning sent a note requesting Payne to meet him. Payne took it for a challenge, and went in expectation of a duel. But to his surprise, Washington rose to meet him and said with a smile, "Mr. Payne, to err is human; but to correct our errors is always honorable. I believe I was wrong yesterday. You have had, I think, some satisfaction, and if you think that's enough, here is my hand—let us be friends." Payne became from that moment an enthusiastic friend and admirer of Washington, who, in all his victories, never won a more glorious triumph than when by ruling his own spirit he subdued the anger of his enemy and won his confidence and love.

THE WEIGHT OF JUDGMENT

A rich man once seized the small field of a poor widow in order to add it to the gardens of his estate. The poor woman went to the judge, to whom she told her story. The judge saddled his horse, hung a large sack on its back, and rode off to the rich man's estate.

He found the rich man walking in his newly acquired land. The judge dismounted and said, "Excuse me, sir. Can I fill this sack with dirt from these grounds?" The rich man assented. When the sack was filled the judge asked the rich man to help him lift it onto the horse's back. The sack, however, was too heavy. "I can't do it," said the rich man; "it's impossible."

"Sir," said the judge, "this sack contains a small portion of the earth you took from the poor widow. If you can't lift this portion of earth, how will you bear the weight of having taken all of it when Judgment Day comes?"

WHY SHOULD I REPENT?

We: Dear Father, whenever the end is scheduled to be, can't you give us an extension of time?"

He: Willingly. But tell me first, what will you do with it?

We: Well...ah...we will go on doing pretty much what we have been doing; after all, isn't that why we are asking for an extension?

He: And isn't that exactly why I want to end it soon—because you show no inclination to change? Why should I reverse the order of nature so that you can go on doing the very things I want to put an end to?

We: But is what we are doing so terribly wrong? The economy seems sound enough. Why shouldn't we go on doing the things which have made this country great?

He: Haven't I made it clear enough to you what kind of greatness I expect of my offspring? Forget the statistics; you are capable of better things. Your stirring commercials don't impress me in the least.

We: But why should we repent when all we are doing is what each considers to be for the best good of himself and the nation?

He: Because it is not you but I who decide what that shall be, and I have told you a hundred times what is best for you individually and collectively—and that is repentance, no matter who you are.

We: We find your inference objectionable, sir—quite unacceptable.

He: I know.

—*Hugh Nibley*
Intellectual Autobiography

YEARS THAT COUNT

An old man had been invited to dine with friends. At his friends' house, one of them asked him how old he was.

"Four," he answered.

"Come on now," said the friend. "Quit joking. How old are you really?"

"I'm not joking," said the old man. "I am four years old. I've wasted eighty years in foolishness and sinful pleasures and in acquiring wealth, none of which I can take with me when I leave this world. I've only spent four years serving my fellowman. As far as I'm concerned, these four years are the only years of my life worth counting."

YOU HIT MY NEIGHBOR

I remember making a talk in Idaho one time on repentance. Repentance is fundamental to us, as you all know, but after I got through, a fine old brother walked up to me and he said, "Brother Ivins, that was wonderful. You hit my neighbor right square on top of the head."

And a young man followed him up and said, "Brother Ivins, it was good, and you were talking to me all the time."

—*Antoine R. Ivins*

CONSCIENCE

Yet still there whispers the small voice within,
Heard through gain's silence, and over glory's
 din:
Whatever creed be taught or land be trod,
Man's conscience is the oracle of God.

—*Lord Byron*

CONSCIENCE AND FUTURE JUDGMENT

I sat alone with my conscience
In a place where time had ceased,

And we talked of my former living
In the land where the years increased,
And I felt I should have to answer
The question it put to me,
And to face the answer and question
Through all eternity.

The ghost of forgotten actions
Came floating before my sight,
And things that I thought were dead things
Were alive with a terrible might;
And the vision of all my past life
Was an awful thing to face,
Alone with my conscience, sitting
In that solemn, silent place.

And I know of the future Judgment,
How dreadful soever it be,
To sit alone with my conscience
Will be judgment enough for me.
                    —Charles William Stubbs

IT'S HISTORY

The past with all its errors
Can destroy you if you let it.
Learn the lesson from the past
And then the past—forget it.
                    —Richard Devon Walker

OPPORTUNITY

They do me wrong who say I come no more
When once I knock and fail to find you in;
For every day I stand outside your door
And bid you wake, and rise to fight and win.

Wail not for precious chances passed away!
Weep not for golden ages on the wane.
Each night I burn the records of the day,
At sunrise every soul is born again.

Though deep in mire, wring not your hands and
    weep:
I lend my arm to all who say, "I can!"
No shamefaced outcast ever sank so deep,
But yet might rise and be again a man!
                    —Walter Malone

THE PORCUPINE

The past is like a porcupine
Who's lost his pack of needles;
And no matter how the porky whines,
No matter how he wheedles,
He cannot put them back again.
He has to start from scratch.
He has to live in now, not then,
And grow another batch.
                    —Richard Devon Walker

Sabbath

THE DAY OF REST

Stonewall Jackson never mailed a letter without calculating whether it would have to travel on Sunday to reach its place of destination, and if so, he would not mail it until Monday morning. Still further did he carry his Sabbath observance. Unnumbered times have I known him to receive important letters so late on Saturday night that he would not break his fixed resolution never to use his eyes, which were very delicate, by artificial light. He would carry the letters in his pocket until Monday morning, then rise with the sun to read them.

In the winter of 1861-62, while Jackson's forces were at Winchester, he sent a brigade to destroy the canal leading to Washington. The expedition proved a failure, and he attributed it, in some measure, to the fact that Sunday had been needlessly trespassed upon. So when a second expedition was planned he determined there should be no Sabbath-breaking connected with it that he could prevent. The advance was to be made early on Monday morning. On Saturday he ordered my husband (Colonel Preston, at that time on his staff) to see that the necessary powder was in readiness. The quartermaster could not find a sufficient quantity in Winchester on Saturday, but during Sunday it was procured. On Sunday evening the fact in some way got to Jackson's ears. At a very early hour on Monday he dispatched an officer to Shepherdstown for more powder, which was brought. Then summoning Colonel Preston, he said very decisively:

"Colonel, I want you to see that the powder which is used for this expedition is not the powder that was bought on Sunday."

—M. Preston

AN EFFECTIVE MEETING

A man once came home from a sacrament meeting at which he had been very touched. He had felt the Spirit strongly and enjoyed the talks given. His wife, who had stayed home that day, asked him to tell her what had been said.

"Actually," said the man, "I remember practically nothing of what was said. But it made me resolve to live better, and by gum, I will!"

A FORGETFUL FAMILY

A bishop was walking home from church one day and noticed one of his ward members out working in his yard. The member, seeing the bishop, stopped working and asked, "Hello, Bishop. Have you seen my son? He's probably playing basketball up the street. You know him, don't you?"

"I think I saw him," said the bishop. "A boy with a short memory, isn't he?"

"What makes you think he has a short memory?" asked the man, with a look of wonder.

"I think he has," said the bishop, "and I think he must belong to a family that has short memories."

"What in the world makes you think so?"

"Because," said the bishop, "God has said, 'Remember the Sabbath Day to keep it holy,' and it appears that the boy and his family have forgotten all about it."

GO FOR YOU AND ME

There was a man who avoided going to church on Sundays, but would send his wife, saying, "Go for you and me."

One night he had a dream that both he and his wife were dead and had gone up to the gates of heaven. An angel came to the gate and let the wife in. When the husband asked why he could not enter, the angel replied, "She's gone in for both herself and you."

HAPPY TO FEEL

A Dutch brother by the name of Folkers was living with his wife at my place, and they could not speak or understand the English language. He used to go to the fast meetings, and when the other people talked, he could not understand what they said. When they finished, he would get up and talk, and we could not understand him. One day I asked him, "Why do you go to the English-speaking services? You cannot understand." It took me some time to make him understand what I wanted to know. Finally, he smiled and said: "It is not what you hear that makes you happy; not what you see that makes you happy; it is what you feel, and I can feel just as well as anybody."

—*George Albert Smith*

I GO IN EMPTY AND COME OUT FULL

A poor woman faithfully went to church every week. Her husband, however, was not so devoted. Week after week she encouraged him to go, but he would not. Finally tired of her pestering him, he asked, "Why do you keep going to church? Give me a good reason."

"I can't explain to you why I go," she said. "All I can tell you is that I go in empty and come out full."

I TRAVEL FURTHER THIS WAY

During the last century a traveler rode up to an inn where he spent the night. The next day was Sunday, and he was asked whether he would continue his journey that day.

"No," he answered.

"Why not?"

"Because," he said, "I'm on a long journey, and wish to perform it as soon as I can. I've long been accustomed to travel on horseback, and have found that, if I stop on the Sabbath, my horse will travel farther during the week than if I do not."

READ THE WHOLE COMMANDMENT

A rich young man decided that life was too good to be spent working. Six days a week he enjoyed himself, sleeping in, relaxing, doing as he pleased. On the seventh he would go to church, but the effects of the other six days began to show up. He would sometimes leave meetings early, or fall asleep.

His bishop, beginning to worry about him, went to visit him. After talking to him for a while, he asked, "How are you doing on your Sabbath observance?"

"I'm doing fine."

"Then you remember the Sabbath day and keep it holy?"

"Yes."

"Then," answered the bishop, "you haven't read the rest of the commandment: Six days shalt thou labor, and do all thy work, and so on, for if a man does not labor six days of the week, he is not likely to rest properly on the seventh."

SABBATH EXAMPLE

John Adams, while President of the United States, as he was returning from the country to his family in Boston, was interrupted by a New England snowstorm which blocked his way. He was then at Andover, twenty miles from Boston. Sunday morning the roads became for a time passable. He was encouraged to continue his journey. The circumstances of his detention and the sickness of his family would justify his traveling on the Sabbath.

"No," he said, "the justifiable occasion would not prevent my traveling on the Sabbath from being a bad example."

He therefore decided to wait until Monday.

SABBATH HABITS

A lady had a Scotch terrier which always accompanied her to church on Sunday, waiting outside until the meeting was over. One summer the lady and her family took a several-week vacation, leaving the dog behind. The dog, however, continued to come to church by itself for several Sundays in a row. After waiting in the churchyard the proper amount of time, it would quietly make the three-mile trip home.

—*Mr. Jesse*

SUNDAY SAINTS

A country bishop said to his congregation, "Brethren and sisters, when you leave the church just take a look at the ducks. They're beautiful ducks and they'll swim around in their pond, splashing and playing and washing themselves until they're soaking wet. Then you'll see them swim to shore and they'll give their wings a bit of a flap and they'll be dry again. Now, my friends, you come here every Sunday and have a good shower of the gospel until you're pretty well soaking wet. But you just go home, sit down by your fireplace, give your wings a bit of a flap and you're as dry as ever again."

TRAVELING RIGHT

A man started from Connecticut with his family for Ohio. He was on the road about four weeks, and rested every Sabbath. From morning to night others, journeying the same way, passed him by. Before the close of the week, however, he had passed them. Those who went by late on the Sabbath he passed on Monday; those who went by a little earlier he passed on Tuesday; and so on, until before the next Sabbath he had passed them all. His horses were no better than theirs, nor were they better fed. But having had the benefit of resting on the Sabbath, according to the law of God, they could out-travel those who had violated that law.

WHAT THE LAW REQUIRES

A businessman was once approached by a ferry company, with a fine prospect of a lucrative business. They asked him to invest in their stock. He, however, declined because they ran their boats on the Sabbath.

"We are required by law to do so," was the company's response.

"Yes," he replied, "I know that the law requires you to run your boats on the Sabbath, but the law does not require me to invest my money in your stock."

BREAD OF THE WORLD

Bread of the world in mercy broken,
Wine of the soul in mercy shed,
By whom the words of life were spoken,
And in whose death our sins are dead:

Look on the heart by sorrow broken,
Look on the tears by sinners shed;
And be Thy feast to us the token
That by Thy grace our souls are fed.
—Reginald Heber

Scriptures

AN ATHEIST'S ARGUMENT

Voltaire brought an argument to show that the Bible story of the golden calf being dissolved was an impossibility—a chemical impossibility. While Voltaire was proving that gold could not be held in solution, all the gilders and coiners and metallurgists of the earth were holding gold in solution, and there were fifty shops in Paris at that time where Voltaire might have seen the very process which he professed did not exist.

BIBLICAL AND SCIENTIFIC MIRACLES

I was talking with a man one day, and he said he could not accept the statements in the scriptures about the fall of Adam, and death being brought into the world. He could not believe in the miracles recorded in the scriptures.

He said to believe that Joshua commanded the sun and the moon to stand still and that Jonah was swallowed by a fish was unscientific. "You cannot expect me to believe such things as these."

He thought himself consistent with reason, and that I was inconsistent. All of you go back with me, in imagination, to the year 1830, when the Church was organized.

Suppose I tell you—in 1830—that in the number of years between 1830 and today—that the scientific marvels that we now know would be commonplace. Will you accept that more quickly than the story of Joshua or of Jonah? In 1830, which story would you accept first?

—*Joseph Fielding Smith*

BUTTERFLIES AND BEES

To some the Bible is uninteresting and unprofitable, because they read too fast. Among the insects which subsist on the sweet sap of flowers, there are two very different classes. One is remarkable for its beauty. It dances from flower to flower and you cannot help admiring its grace, for it is plainly covering a great deal of ground. But in the same field there is another worker whose brown attire and businesslike attitude may not be so attractive. His fluttering neighbor darts here and there, and sips elegantly wherever he can find a drop of ready nectar; but this dingy plodder makes a point of alighting everywhere, and wherever he alights he either finds honey or makes it. If the flower-cup is deep, he goes down to the bottom. If its dragon-mouth is shut, he opens it. His painted rival has no patience for such dull and long-winded details. But where does it end? Why, the one died last October along with the flowers. The other is warm in his hive during the winter, surrounded by the stores he's gathered. To which do you belong—the butterflies or bees? Do you search the scriptures, or do you only skim them?

—*Dr. Hamilton*

DIAMONDS AND ANGELS

A young man once long ago claimed he had found a large diamond in his field as he was ploughing. He put the stone on display to the public free of charge, and everyone took sides. A psychologist showed, by citing some famous case studies, that the young man was suffering from a well-known form of delusion. An historian showed that other men have also claimed to have found diamonds in fields and been deceived. A geologist proved that there were no diamonds in the area, but only quartz. The young man had been fooled by a quartz. When asked to inspect the stone itself, the geologist declined with a weary, tolerant smile and a kindly shake of the head. An English professor showed that the young man in describing the stone used the very same language that others had used in describing uncut diamonds. He was, therefore, simply speaking the common language of his time. A sociologist showed that only three out of 177 florists' assistants in four major cities believed the stone was genuine. A clergyman wrote a book to show that it was not the young man but someone else who had found the stone.

Finally an indigent jeweler named Snite pointed out that since the stone was still available for examination the answer to the question of whether it was a diamond or not had absolutely nothing to do with who found it, or whether the finder was honest or sane, or who believed him, or whether he would know a diamond from a brick, or whether diamonds had ever been found in fields, or whether people had ever been fooled by quartz or glass, but was to be answered simply and solely by putting the stone to certain well-known tests for diamonds.

Experts on diamonds were called in. Some of them declared it genuine. The others made nervous jokes about it and declared that they could not very well jeopardize their dignity and reputations by appearing to take the thing too seriously. To hide the bad impression thus made, someone came out with the theory that the stone was really a synthetic diamond, very skillfully made, but a fake just the same. The objection to this is that the production of a good synthetic diamond 120 years ago would have been an even more remarkable feat than the finding of a real one.

—Hugh Nibley
Lehi in the Desert

THE GIFT OF TONGUES

A lady once went to sacrament meeting and, as usual, took along her scriptures so she could turn to any passage that the speaker might happen to refer to. But she found that she had no use for her scriptures there, and on coming home said to a friend, "I should have left my scriptures home today and brought my dictionary. The way he was speaking you'd think he had the gift of tongues."

JOHNNY HAD READ THE BIBLE

Johnny was his name, and he had a little brother named Billy. The two were playing in their mother's yard. Johnny was whittling a stick, and Billy had just caught a fly. "Johnny," said he, "what a funny thing a fly is. See what lots of legs he's got. And every time I blow on him he buzzes. I wonder how God made him?"

Johnny had an idea of how God made the fly. He went on whittling, and said, "Well, Billy, God don't make flies like men make houses. When he wants flies he says, 'Let there be flies,' and then there is flies."

Johnny had read the Bible and understood it.

—Orson F. Whitney

PARLEY P. PRATT AND THE BOOK OF MORMON

I opened it (the Book of Mormon) with eagerness, and read its title page. I then read the testimony of several witnesses in relation to the manner of its being found and translated. After this I commenced its contents by course. I read all day; eating was a burden, for I had no desire for food; sleep was a burden when the night came, for I preferred reading to sleep.

As I read, the Spirit of the Lord was upon me, and I knew and comprehended that the book was true, as plainly and manifestly as a man comprehends and knows that he exists. My joy was now full, as it were, and I rejoiced sufficiently to more than pay me for all the sorrows, sacrifices and toils of my life. I soon determined to see the young man who had been the instrument of its discovery and translation.

—Parley P. Pratt

PROVE IT!

A woman was sitting on a park bench reading the Bible when she was approached by another woman, an atheist.

"What are you reading there?" asked the atheist.

"It's the word of God," said the reader.

"The word of God! Well, what do you know. And who told you it was the word of God?"

"He told me so Himself."

"Have you ever spoken with Him, then?"

The poor woman felt embarrassed because she wasn't used to defending herself. At last she exclaimed, looking upward, "Can you prove to me that there is a sun in the sky?"

"Prove it! Why, the best proof is that it warms me, and that I can see its light."

"So it is with me," said the reader. "The proof of this book's being the word of God is that it warms and lights my soul."

READING WELL

A theological student who had a very high opinion of his own talent on one occasion asked a speech professor, "What do I especially need to learn in this department?"

"You just need to learn to read," said the professor.

"Oh, I can read now," replied the student.

The professor handed the young man a new testament, pointed to Luke 24:25 and asked him to read it. The student read, "Then he said unto them, O fools, and slow of heart to *believe* all that the prophets have spoken."

"Ah," said the professor, "they were fools for *believing* the prophets, were they?"

Of course that was not right, and so the young man tried again.

"O fools, and slow of heart to believe *all* that the prophets have spoken."

"The prophets, then, were sometimes liars?" asked the professor.

"No. O fools, and slow of heart to believe all that the *prophets* have spoken."

"According to this reading," the professor suggested, "the prophets were notorious liars."

This was not a satisfactory conclusion, and so he tried again. "O fools, and slow of heart to believe all that the prophets *have spoken.*"

"I see now," said the professor, "the prophets wrote the truth, but they *spoke lies.*"

This last criticism discouraged the student, and he admitted that he did not know how to read. The difficulty lies in the fact that the words "slow of heart to believe" apply to the whole of the latter part of the sentence, and emphasis on any particular word entirely destroys the meaning. There are thousands of passages that may be rendered meaningless, or even ridiculous, by the change of emphasis upon a single word alone.

SEEING WITH YOUR OWN EYES

When I was young I read the Bible over and over and over again, and was so perfectly acquainted with it that I could, in an instant, have pointed to any verse that might have been mentioned. I then read the commentators; but I soon threw them aside, for I found therein many things my conscience could not approve, as being contrary to the sacred text. It's always better to see with your own eyes than with those of other people.

—*Martin Luther*

SO OUR SOULS CAN EAT

"Mamma," said a little girl, "why do you read the scriptures so much?"

"I need to," said the mother. "Why do you eat?"

"You know I need to eat," said the girl, "or else I'd die."

"What has God given us besides the body?" asked the mother.

"Our souls?" asked the girl.

"That's right," said the mother. "What would die without food?"

"Our bodies," said the girl.

"You see, dear, my soul needs food as much as my body does. And where will I find food for my soul?"

"Ah, now I understand!" exclaimed the girl. "We must read the scriptures every day so our souls can eat."

TWO STRINGS TO OUR BOW

An atheist was making fun of a country peasant's belief in the Bible. The peasant calmly said, "We country people like to have two strings to our bow."

"What do you mean?" asked the atheist.

"Only this," answered the man, "that believing the Bible and acting up to it is like having two strings to one's bow; because if it is not true, I'll be a better man for living according to it, and so it will be for my good in this life— that is one string to my bow—and if it should be true, it will be better for me in the next life—that is another string, and a pretty strong one it is. But sir, if you do not believe in the Bible, and, on that account, do not live as it requires, you have not one string to your bow. And oh, sir, if its tremendous threatenings prove true—oh, think what then will become of you!"

—*Caughey*

WHY SO MUCH?

A kind old woman was always seen reading the scriptures. Others found this interesting, and one day a neighbor asked her why she read her scriptures as much as she did?

"Because I can't find time to read them more often," she said.

————————

YES, I BELIEVE IT

In the eighteenth century an African prince visited England. While there a friend presented him with a Bible and went to great lengths to convince him that it was the word of God. Did the friend's arguments convince the prince?

Later in his visit he was asked about the Bible. Did he believe it? If so, why?

"Yes, I believe it," said the Prince. "But it wasn't the arguments that convinced me. When I came here and found that all good men believed in the Bible and all bad men did not I was then sure that the Bible must be what good men call it—the word of God."

————————

SOME DAY OR OTHER

Some day or other I shall surely come
Where true hearts wait for me;
Then let me learn the language of that home
While here on earth I be,
Lest my poor lips for want of words be dumb
In that High Company.

—*Louise Chandler Moulton*

————————

Word of Wisdom

THE BAD LUMP

A frequent visitor to a certain bar finally decided that he'd had enough and swore off alcohol. The barkeeper laughed at him.

"You'll never be able to do it."

"I think I will," said the man.

"I'll bet you fifty dollars you can't," said the barkeeper. "If at the end of a year you haven't taken a drink, you win the bet."

When the year was up, the man returned to the bar.

"Well," said the barkeeper, "how did you do?"

"I made it," said the man, "But I have had a growing lump here on one side of my stomach."

"I knew that giving up drinking would be bad for your health. You'd better have a drink. If that lump keeps growing, you may die of it."

"Oh, I don't know," said the man. He reached down to his stomach and pulled a large bag from under his shirt. "I've been saving the money I would have spent here. I now have several hundred dollars. I *want* this lump to keep growing."

———

THE CARPENTER AND THE LICENSE

A carpenter who was tired of carpentry decided that he wanted to get rich and the fastest way he could think of was to open a bar. He went to a friend of his to ask if he would cosign the license he would need to open the bar.

"I don't know," said the friend. "Don't you think you'd just be making it easier for more people to become drunkards?"

"Perhaps I shall," said the carpenter.

"Don't you think that at least five men a year will die drunkards if you succeed in getting the license?"

"Why, I never thought of that before, but I suppose that would be so."

"Then if the Lord lets you keep the bar for ten years, fifty men will have died because of you.

Now what becomes of the drunkard? Does he go to heaven?"

"I suppose not," said the carpenter.

"I'm sure he doesn't, for no drunkard shall inherit the kingdom of heaven. What becomes of him then?"

"Why, I suppose he goes to hell."

"Well, don't you think it would be just of the Lord if, at the end of ten years, He sends you to hell too, to look after those fifty drunkards?"

The man gave up his attempt at a license and went back to carpentry, quite content with his honest occupation.

———

A CHANGE OF CONDUCT

A few years ago a young man and a young woman were talking. He, a smoker, insisted that a person could use six cigarettes within a twenty-four-hour period and that the amount of stimulants that the body could absorb from this indulgence was so negligible in its effects upon the organs of the body that it could not be detected by scientific measurements. He was urging her to take up smoking in order that she might be able to appear less conspicuous when in company with others who smoked. The girl attempted to refute the arguments, but for each declaration that she made against his arguments he replied with a rebuttal that appeared to destroy her point of view.

Finally, in rather a state of desperation, she made this statement:

"Suppose that what you say is true. Suppose I can smoke six cigarettes a day without having any harmful effects on either body or mind; and suppose that I can control myself so that I can continue to limit my daily consumption to six cigarettes a day, which I very much doubt after observing how many you and others who have acquired the habit smoke each day; now tell me what I would then have that I don't have now except a foul-smelling breath, yellow-stained fingers, a little less femininity, and less money in my purse? If there is anything the smoking of six cigarettes will give me to offset these factors, I might be interested.''

The young man made no reply. What could be gained by a change of conduct?

—*T. Edgar Lyon*

THE DRINKING KING

Philip, king of Macedon, often bragged about his ability to drink freely.

Demosthenes, hearing him once spoke up quickly, ''Pardon me, sire. Drinking freely is a good quality in a sponge, but not in a king.''

DRINKING MODERATELY

A man decided he would drink no more. He didn't like the state of drunkenness he'd find himself in after a drinking spree.

His friends, however, told him he was being drastic. He needn't be so hard on himself. They convinced him to sign a contract that would limit him to drinking moderately at home.

In a few days he was brought home stone drunk. When he sobered up he called his friends together and ripped up the contract in their presence. ''I started out with good intentions,'' he said, ''but after I'd had a thimbleful of alcohol, I was out of control and I couldn't stop.''

The man then drew up another contract that would not allow him to ever take a drop of alcohol.

THE DRUNKEN COUNTERPART

The wife of a drunkard once found her husband in a filthy condition, with torn clothes, matted hair, bruised face, asleep in the kitchen, having come home from a drunken revel. She sent for a photographer, and had a portrait of him taken in all his wretched appearance, and placed it on the mantel beside another portrait taken at the time of his marriage, which showed him handsome and well dressed, as he had been in other days. When he was sober again he saw the two pictures, awakened to a consciousness of his condition, and gave up drinking to begin a better life.

DRUNKEN MONKEYS

Like men, monkeys are easily outwitted when under the influence of liquor. In Darfour and Sena, Africa, the natives make a fermented beer, of which the monkeys are passionately fond. Aware of this, the natives go to parts of the forest frequented by the monkeys, and set on the ground gourds full of the enticing liquor. As soon as a monkey sees and tastes it he utters loud cries of joy that soon attract his comrades. Then a party begins, and in a short time they all show degrees of intoxication. Then the men appear. Most of the drinkers are too far gone to distrust them, and apparently take them for a larger species of monkey. When a man takes one by the hand to lead him off, the nearest monkey will cling to the one who thus finds a support, and endeavor to go on also. Another will clutch at him, and so on until the man leads a staggering line of ten or a dozen tipsy monkeys. When finally brought to the village, they are securely caged and gradually sobered.

A FIFTY-CENT PROFIT

A grocer sold a drunkard a bottle of whiskey, according to the law, and made fifty cents profit. The drunkard then, while intoxicated, shot his son-in-law, and his imprisonment ended up costing over twenty thousand dollars a year, which sober men had to earn by the sweat of their brows—all so a grocer could make a fifty-cent profit. Is it fair?

FUNDING A BUSINESS

A young man wanted to start a business and needed to borrow some money. He went to a wealthy man, explained his plan and asked for a loan. The wealthy man asked, ''Do you drink?''

''Occasionally,'' answered the young man.

''Stop it. Stop it for a year and then come back and see me.''

The young man quit drinking at once and at the end of the year returned to the wealthy man.

''Do you smoke?'' asked the wealthy man.

''Yes, now and then,'' answered the young man.

''Stop it. Stop it for a year and then come back and see me.''

The young man immediately quit smoking and after another twelve months returned to see the wealthy man.

"Do you chew tobacco?" asked the wealthy man.

"Yes," said the young man.

"Stop it for a year and then come back and see me."

The young man went away and never returned. When someone asked him why he didn't make one more effort, he replied, "Didn't I know what he was driving at? He'd have told me that as I had stopped chewing, drinking, and smoking, I must have saved enough money to start myself."

_____

GIVING IT UP

A country minister, after delivering the week's sermon, went out on the church steps, pulled out a cigarette, and began to smoke. A member of the church immediately came up to him and chastised him, saying that he could not expect members of the congregation to repent of their sins if the minister indulged in this sin himself.

"I know it's wrong," said the minister. "I've often resolved to give up the habit, but I don't have the strength to do it."

"Why," said the member, "that's the exact excuse others give for not repenting of their sins."

"Well, I'll think it over as I go home," said the minister, "and perhaps I'll give it up."

"That won't do," replied the member, "for you never allow this from the pulpit. You always exhort us to repent on the spot. You never tell us to go home and repent, nor do we pray that we may repent when we get home."

"I see you've got me," said the minister. "I'll try to give up smoking then."

"But," said the member, "that won't do either. You never urge us to try to give up our sins, do you?"

"Why, no. I think it's wrong to suggest that they can't do it at once."

"Will you then practice what you preach, or let your conduct prove you a liar?"

"OK, OK," conceded the minister. "I'm quitting right now." And he took out his pack of cigarettes, dumped them on the ground and buried them in the dirt with his foot.

_____

I AM NOT THAT WEAK

I labored, as you know, much in the mission field. I presided over two missions. We had many Saints who had used tobacco and tea and coffee, and some of them liquor, all of their lives, and it was hard for some of them to quit.

I remember being in one meeting with a stalwart man sitting right down in front of me, and as I read these words, "Adapted to the capacity of the weak and the weakest of all saints who are or can be called saints" (Doctrine and Covenants 89:3), I said: "If there are any Latter-day Saints in this mission weaker than that we will not ask them to keep the Word of Wisdom."

At the close of the meeting, that big fellow came up and said, "President Richards, I am not that weak."

I said, "I didn't think you were. I just wanted to let you know what the Lord had to say about this principle."

—LeGrand Richards

_____

I CAN'T THINK OF A GOOD REASON

Once I was driving along and had two young men with me in my car and a young man thumbed a ride with us. I asked the boys that were with me if we should take him with us and they said yes.

I picked him up, and after we had driven along a little way he said, "Do you mind if I smoke in your car?"

I said, "No, not at all, if you can give me any good reason why you should smoke." And I said, "I will go farther than that." (I was a stake president at this time.) "If you can give me a good reason why you should smoke, I will smoke with you."

Well, these two young men looked at me and wondered. We drove on for some distance, about twenty minutes, I think, and I turned and said:

"Aren't you going to smoke?"

And he said, "No."

I said, "Why not?"

"I can't think of a good reason why I should."

—N. Eldon Tanner

_____

MATTHEW HALE'S VOW

It is recorded as a singular fact in Matthew Hale's life that, at a time when reeling judges and drunken lawyers were common, he would not so much as drink to one's health. His temperance principles were suddenly but firmly formed.

When a young man, he and a friend had a drinking contest. The friend, overcome by the liquor, dropped senseless upon the floor.

Young Hale was horrified, for his friend apparently was dying. Falling upon his knees, he begged God to restore his friend. Vowing to live a temperate life, he asked for strength to overcome his love for strong drinks. He rose from his knees an altered man.

In those days men who mixed with society were compelled to drink "toasts" and "healths." A full goblet of wine must be drained each time a toast was given, or when the host asked his guests to drink to the health of some one of the company.

Hale knew that it was trifling with God to pray, "Lead us not into temptation," and then to do that which would lead him to break his resolution. He saw that if he mingled in society and conformed to its customs, he could not keep his vow. He therefore resolved never again to drink to a person's health.

He kept his vow, though his abstinence caused him much persecution. In his old age he urged his grandchildren to follow his example.

THE MONKEY AND HIS MASTER

A man had a pet monkey which he took with him everywhere. One day the man went into a bar and the monkey went with him. The man drank freely. This time he also allowed the monkey to take a little drink, giving him a half-full glass of whiskey. The monkey took the glass and drank it all. Soon he was skipping, hopping, and dancing merrily around the room. The monkey was drunk.

The man found the drunken monkey so amusing that he decided to get him drunk again. The next day he looked for the monkey, but couldn't see him right away. He looked in the monkey's box, and there was the poor animal, crouched down in a heap.

"Come on out of there," said the man. The monkey came out on three legs, with his forepaw on his head. The monkey had a hangover! He was sick for three days.

Finally the monkey was well and the man decided to have some more fun with him. He took him to the bar and tried to get him to drink, but

the monkey hid under the table. The man began to chase him, but the monkey galloped out of the bar and climbed on top of the roof. The man pointed a gun threateningly at the monkey—monkeys are terrified of guns—but the monkey just ran to the other side of the house. The man got a friend to chase the monkey on the other side, but the monkey jumped up to the chimney and climbed into the flue.

The man was beaten. Although he had that monkey for twelve more years, he could never get him to touch another drop of whiskey.

MY CIGARETTE MONEY

A young couple married and set up housekeeping with a few furnishings and a very limited budget. The fellow smoked but had promised to stop after they were married. Then he failed to do it, as he said he couldn't see anything gained by doing so. The fact of the matter was he had become so enslaved that he didn't think he could stop.

His wife, attempting to stretch the budget and furnish the house with a few purchases each month, insisted that it was an expensive habit. She announced one day that if he would not stop smoking she was going to spend a similar amount on herself. Instead of spending it she secured a bank in the form of a goose perched atop a large golden egg. Each day she dropped the price of a package of cigarettes into it, and on the days when he became nervous and smoked more than usual, she doubled the amount. He kidded her about it, telling her that it was such a negligible amount she would never be able to buy very much with it.

Several years had passed, the depression of the 1930s had come, and prices were falling. One day she saw a want ad, hurried off and made the purchase, and when he returned home in the evening he saw a baby grand piano in the living room. He immediately commenced to scold her, telling her that his salary was being reduced, that he could not afford it, and so forth. She simply replied: "Don't get excited; it's all paid for. I bought it with my cigarette money."

He did not believe it, but sat down, did some figuring, and had to admit that she had been able to buy a real bargain with her ready cash, the equivalent of which had been sent up in smoke. Then and there he resolved to quit the habit—which he did for two days. Several years had passed and one day she announced that she was going to Europe during the coming summer. Again he said that they could not afford it. But she replied: "You can't, but I can. I'm going on my cigarette money."

—*T. Edgar Lyon*

NOT YET OLD ENOUGH TO NEED IT

The arguments were heated in the town as an election was coming up which would decide whether alcohol would be sold there. People lined up on both sides.

One old man, well-respected in the community, was approached by those who wanted alcohol sold. Many of the pro-alcohol people were the old man's friends, and were afraid he was beginning to side with the anti-alcohol group.

"Come on, side with us," they urged. "You've taken a nip or two in your life and it hasn't hurt you. Surely you wouldn't want to deny yourself this pleasure for the rest of your days. Besides, when people get old they need a little nip now and then to keep themselves going."

The old man looked calmly at them and said, "For all I know, old people may need a nip now and then, but I'm only ninety-one years old. I'm not yet old enough to need it."

ONLY ONE FAULT

I was riding through a country town in Vermont, when I chanced to notice a group of people in the churchyard, evidently encircling an open grave.

It was a warm day, and I had ridden ten miles. I led the horse under some trees that shaded the road, to allow him to cool and rest.

Presently a villager came towards me, and I said, "There's a funeral today in your town?"

"Yes—his name was Stephen. He was one of the largest-hearted men I ever knew. We owed something to Stephen. He had great abilities, Stephen had. We sent him to the legislature three times. They thought of nominating him for governor. But," he added, "Stephen had one fault."

I made no answer. I was tired and watched the people slowly disperse.

"A very generous man, Stephen was. Always visited the sick. The old people all liked him.

Even the children used to follow him in the streets."

"A good man, indeed," I said, indifferently.

"Yes. He only had one fault."

"What was that?" I asked.

"He drank."

"Did it harm him?"

"Yes, somewhat. He didn't seem to have any power to resist it at last. He got behind and had to mortgage his farm, and finally had to sell it. His wife died on account of the reverse; kind of crushed, disappointed. Then his children, not having the right bringing up, turned out badly. His intemperance seemed to take away their spirit. He had to leave politics; it wouldn't do, you see. Then we had to set him aside from church, and at last his habits brought on paralysis and we had to take him to the poorhouse. He died there; only forty-five. There were none of his children at the funeral. Poor man, he had only one fault."

"Only one fault!"

The ship had only one leak, but it went down.

"Only one fault!"

The temple had only one decaying pillar, but it fell.

"Only one fault." Home gone, wife lost, family ruined, honor forfeited, social and religious privileges abandoned; broken health, poverty, paralysis and the poorhouse.

One fault, only one.

THE REFORMED CROWS

A farmer had one of the best farms on the Illinois river. About one hundred acres of it were covered with waving corn. When spring came, the crows seemed determined to destroy the entire crop. When one was killed, it seemed as though a dozen came to its funeral. And though the sharp crack of a rifle often drove them away, they always returned with its echo. The farmer at length became weary of playing around and decided on a new technique. He bought a gallon of alcohol, in which he soaked several quarts of corn, and scattered it over the field. The crows came and partook with their usual relish, and as usual, they were pretty well loaded. And you should have seen the cooing and cackling, the strutting and swaggering! When the boys attempted to catch them, they laughed at the crows' staggering gait and the way the crows flew zigzag through the air. At length the crows reached the edge of the woods, and gathered together, cackled their praises—or curses—of alcohol. And the farmer saved his corn. As soon as the crows became sober they became very temperate. Not one kernal of corn would they touch in that field.

TIMING IT

A minister once found one of his congregation drunk. The next day he called him on the carpet to reprove him for it.

"It's wrong to get drunk," said the minister.

"I know that," said the guilty person, "but I don't drink as much as you do."

"What, sir! How is that?"

"Why, didn't you have a glass of whiskey after dinner?"

"Why yes. I take a little whiskey after dinner to help my digestion."

"And don't you take a little whiskey before you go to bed at night?"

"Yes, sure. I just take a little at night to help me sleep!"

"Well," continued the member, "that's just fourteen glasses a week, and about sixty every month. I only get paid off once a month, and then if I'd take sixty glasses I'd be dead drunk for a week, if I weren't dead. Now the only difference is, you time it better than I do!"

USED

"What have I done," cried an old woman, "to be used so?"

"Be used? How?" a friend asked.

"He," she said, pointing to a bar up the street, "that barkeeper, took my husband, as faithful a man as ever married a woman, tore up his heart, ruined his body, deadened his tongue, and sent him home to inflict on me all the curses which hung over his guilty head. And because of that man my husband is now dead.

"And then my son caught the spirit and followed the example of his father. He was led by that same barkeeper into that bar where he spent every cent he earned or could beg or steal from me, until he became a useless criminal. He too was killed by that barkeeper.

"And now here I am, widowed, childless and

old and that barkeeper continues to operate while other murderers are in jail where they can do no more harm. What have I done that I should be used so?"

The friend, touched, said, "God will not allow the cry of the widow to go unheard."

TOBACCO
(SUPPOSED TO BE WRITTEN BY A YOUNG BEGINNER)

This Indian weed, that once did grow
On fair Virginia's fertile plain,
From whence it came—again may go,
To please some happier swain:
Of all the plants that Nature yields
This, least beloved, shall shun my fields.

In evil hour I first essayed
To chew this vile forbidden leaf,
When, half ashamed, and half afraid,
I touched, and tasted—to my grief:
Ah me! the more I was forbid,
The more I wished to take a quid.

But when I smoked, in thought profound,
And raised the spiral circle high,
My heart grew sick, my head turned round—
And what can all this mean, (said I)—
Tobacco surely was designed
To poison, and destroy mankind.

Unhappy they, whom choice, or fate
Inclines to prize this bitter weed;
Perpetual source of female hate;
On which no beast but man will feed;
That sinks my heart, and turns my head,
And sends me, reeling, home to bed!
—*Nancy Sullivan*

WINE IS LIKE ANGER

Wine is like anger, for it makes
    us strong,
Blind and impatient, and it leads
    us wrong;
The strength is quickly lost;
We feel the error long.
—*Crabb*

Work

ARABIC PRESCRIPTION FOR
SLEEPLESSNESS

An English doctor, traveling in the Middle
East, studied the native methods for curing dis-
eases. On one occasion when traveling in the
Sahara, he asked an old sheik, "What do you do
with sick people when they can't sleep?"

He received the practical reply, "We set them
to guard the camels."

ASA AND IRA

Asa and Ira were two brothers whose farms lay
side by side in a fertile valley. When the corn, the
oats and the barley were springing up, the weeds
also came up in the rich soil. "Do you see," said
Asa, "how the weeds are growing? There is a
danger of their choking out the crops entirely."

"Well, well, we must accept it," replied Ira.
"Weeds as well as grain are part of the Creator's
plan. There is no use murmuring about them."
And he lay down for his usual afternoon doze.

"I can only be resigned to what I cannot
help," said Asa. So he went to work and plowed
and hoed until his fields were clear of weeds.

"The armyworms are nearby," said Asa to Ira
one day. "They've already eaten through the
adjoining meadows, and are moving towards us."

"Ah!" exclaimed Ira. "They will destroy what
the weeds have not choked out. I will immediately
pray that they may be stopped or turned aside."

But Asa replied, "I pray every morning for
strength to do the work of the day." Then he
hurried to dig a trench around his land which the
armyworms could not pass, while Ira returned
late, saving only a small portion of his crops from
the ravages.

"Do you see, Ira?" said Asa on another morning. "The river is rising fast. There is only a
slender chance of preventing our farms from
being flooded."

"It's judgment upon us for our sins, and what
can we do?" cried Ira, throwing himself in despair
upon the ground.

"There are no judgments so severe as those
which our own laziness brings upon us," replied
Asa. And he went quickly and hired workmen,
with whose help he raised an embankment that
withstood the flood, while Ira witnessed, with
blank looks and folded hands, the destruction of
his harvests.

"There is one consolation," he said. "My
children, at least, are left for me."

But while most of Asa's children grew up
strong and good people, Ira's children were often
in trouble, never having learned how to work.

"The ways of the Lord are not equal," complained Ira to his brother. "Why are you always
prosperous, while I get all the misfortune?"

"I only know this," replied Asa, "that heaven
has always helped me to treat the faults of my
children as I did the weeds, the caterpillars, and
the flood; and that I have never prayed without
making work the messenger of my prayer."

BEWARE OF THE EVIL TOOL

The father of sin decided to have a sale and
dispose of all his tools to anyone who would pay
his price.

The implements were laid out in a row for
inspection, and among others were tools labeled
Malice, Envy, Hatred, Jealousy, and Deceit.
Every one had a price tag on it. Apart from the
others lay a harmless-looking, wedge-shaped tool,
very much worn from use, that was priced a great
deal higher than the rest.

One of the buyers asked the devil what it was.
"That," he answered, "is Discouragement; and
it's in fine shape."

"But why have you priced it so high?"

"Because it is more useful to me than any of
the others. I can pry open and get inside a man's
consciousness with that wedge when I couldn't
get near him with any of the others. And believe

me, once I do get inside I can use that man in whatever way suits me best. Of course, you'll notice it is well worn. That's because I use it with nearly everybody, for very few of you mortals know that it belongs to me."

However, the price was so high that this particular tool was never sold. The devil still owns it, and is still using it.

BUT THE OPERATION WAS BRILLIANT!

A group of doctors were at a party discussing their work when a dedicated surgeon was asked how many times he had performed a difficult feat of surgery. He replied that he had performed the operation thirteen times.

Another doctor spoke up, "Ah, but sir, I have performed that operation one hundred sixty times."

The questioner then went on, "And how many times did you save the patient's life?"

The first doctor replied, "I saved eleven of the thirteen." He then turned to the second doctor. "And how many did you save of the hundred sixty?"

"Oh, I lost them all, *but the operation was brilliant!*"

CAST A LINE FOR YOURSELF

A young man stood watching some fishermen on a bridge. He was poor and dejected. At last he approached a basket filled with fish, and sighed, "If I had these I would be happy. I could sell them at a good price and buy some food and lodging."

"I'll give you just as many and just as good fish," said the owner, "if you will do me a small favor."

"What is it?" asked the young man.

"Just tend this line until I come back. I want to run a short errand."

The young man gladly accepted. The old man was gone so long that the young man began to get impatient. Meanwhile the hungry fish snapped greedily at the baited hook, and the young man lost all his depression in the excitement of pulling them in; and when the owner of the line returned he had caught a large number. Presenting them to the young man, the old fisherman said, "I fulfill my promise from the fish you have caught to teach you that whenever you see others earning

what you need, waste no time in fruitless wishing, but cast a line for yourself."

DOING THE WORK

A certain man who is very successful now was very poor when he was a boy. When asked how he became successful, he said, "My father taught me never to play until my work was finished, and never to spend my money until I had earned it. If I had but an hour's work in the day, I must do that the first thing, and in an hour. And after that I was allowed to play; and then I could play with much more pleasure than if I had the thought of an unfinished task before my mind. I early formed the habit of doing everything on time, and it soon became easy to do so. It is to this I owe my success."

THE GARDENER'S LESSON

Two gardeners had their crops of peas killed by the frost. One of them was very impatient under the loss, and fretted about it very much. The other at once patiently went to work to plant a new crop. After a while the impatient, fretting man went to his neighbor. To his surprise, he found a crop of peas thriving. He asked how this could be.

"These are what I sowed while you were fretting," said his neighbor.

"But don't you ever fret?" he asked.

"Yes, I do; but I put it off until I have repaired the mischief that has been done."

"Why, then, you have no need to fret at all."

"True," said his friend, "and that's the reason I put it off."

HONEST LABOR

"I am willing to do anything to get an honest living," said a young man who came into my office asking for work.

"Are you? All right! Take this box to Broadway. Take it on your shoulder, and I'll give you a quarter of a dollar for it, and another job on your return."

The young man looked astounded! "What! make an errand boy of me, sir? I've been well brought up, and am not willing to do anything menial."

"But you said you were willing to do *anything* to get an honest living, did you not? Is there any dishonesty involved in doing this errand? You say you have been 'well brought up.' I doubt it. If you had been you would not have disproved your assertion so speedily. If you had you would have been proud enough of your reputation for honesty to have made your words good, no matter at what cost to your feelings. If you had you would sooner go into the street here as a street cleaner and scavenger than eat the bread of idleness. You ought to remember that he that humbleth himself shall be exalted. I have never known a man capable of rising who did not rise, provided he laid the foundation well. And a sure foundation often involves much digging in the dirt, water and quicksands of life. And even if the quicksands cave in about you, a curb must be made and sunk until you get below them onto solid rock."

My young friend may think of what I said to him, and it may profit him. But he did not heed the lesson then that I tried to give; and while he did not lose a friend, he lost, for the time being, the help I might have given him. For the young man who is not willing to adapt, and not capable of adapting himself to all the circumstances and trials of life, and to climb out of deep, damp places where there can be no easy, carpeted stairways by which to ascend, by dirty ladders, or even hand-over-hand by a slippery rope, is not much of a man nor likely to be. To get through this world requires good, strong, mental muscle, and a moral fiber which is stronger than any false pride that can be created; and I pity young men or women who are so educated as to believe that any honest labor is too menial for them.

Indeed, I have no faith whatever in such people.

I CAN DO AS MUCH AS THEY WILL DO

A seventeen-year-old applied for a job with a road construction gang. He was rather slightly built and the boss eyed him critically. "Afraid you won't do, son," he said. "This is heavy work and you can't keep up with the heavier, older men."

The youngster glanced at the crew leaning on their shovels. "Perhaps I can't do as much as these men *can* do," he replied, "but I certainly can do as much as they *will* do." He got the job.

IDLE YEARS

A hardworking, productive man, suffering from a chronic disease, consulted three doctors, who stated that the disease would eventually result in his death.

"How long," asked the man, "do I have?"

The doctors all replied that if he was careful and quit working he still had about five or six years left.

"And if I keep working?" asked the man.

They all replied, "About two or three years."

"In that case," said the man, "I'll continue working. I'd rather live two or three years in doing some good than living six in idleness."

KEEPING AT IT

After a great snowstorm, a little boy began to shovel a path through a large snowbank in front of his grandmother's door. He had nothing but a small shovel to work with.

"How do you expect to get through that drift?" asked a man passing by.

"By keeping at it," said the boy, cheerfully.

LADY WASHINGTON

Around the time of the Revolutionary War, two ladies were talking.

"Guess what I did?" said one. "I visited Lady Washington, General Washington's wife."

"Oh, really?" exclaimed the other. "Tell me what she was like, what she said, what she did."

"Well, I'll honestly tell you that I was never so ashamed in all my life. Since I had heard that she was such a grand lady I decided I'd better put on my absolutely finest clothes. I dressed myself very elegantly and went to her home. When I was introduced to her I was surprised to find her sitting in the parlor, wearing a checked apron, knitting! She received me very graciously, but after the introductions were over she resumed her knitting. There I was, without a stitch of work, and all dressed up, but General Washington's wife, with her own hands, was knitting stockings for her husband and herself. And that was not all. In the course of the afternoon, she took occasion to say, in a manner that would offend no one, that at this time it was very important that American ladies should be examples of diligence to their countrywomen, because the separation from the mother country will dry up our resources from which we get many of our comforts. We must become independent by our determination to do without what we cannot make for ourselves. While our husbands and brothers are examples of patriotism, we should be patterns of industry."

THE LAZY BEES

Years ago in Miami, Florida, the president of the branch had several beehives. Calling him by name, I asked: "Have you a lot of honey now?"

He answered, "Yes."

"Is it good honey?"

"No," he said, "it is not."

"Why?" I asked.

"Look over yonder," he replied. And I beheld a bottling plant. There were scores of boxes covered with syrup. The bees had become lazy. Instead of flying out into the fields and extracting the nectar from the flowers, they lighted upon the boxes and fed upon the syrup; consequently, the honey wasn't much good.

—*Charles A. Callis*

THE LITTLE PUSH

In an English shipyard a large ship was ready to be launched. A crowd had gathered to see it glide down the slides that were to carry it into the water. The blocks and wedges were knocked away, but the massive hull did not stir. Just then a little boy ran forward and began to push the ship with all his might. The crowd broke out laughing. But it so happened that the ship was just ready to move, and the few pounds pushed by the boy were all that was needed to start it. The ship slid gracefully into the water as the amazed crowd watched.

MORE THAN YOU CAN CATCH UP WITH

While on a trip with a friend through Georgia, I met a local character who spent most of his time on the porch of a "fork-in-the-road" settlement. His slowness of speech and deliberate actions caused me to ask him the why and wherefore of his outstanding characteristics.

"Wal, son," he drawled, "it don't pay nobody to be in a hurry. You always pass up more than you catch up with."

—*Millard Miller*

THE NATURE OF PATIENCE

"Newton, how did you make your great discoveries?" asked a friend one day.

"By always thinking about them," he answered.

Giardini, a great violinist, was once asked by a youth, "How long will it take me to play like you do?"

"Twelve hours a day for twenty years," he replied.

ONE TICK AT A TIME

A little clock had just been finished by a clock-maker and put on a shelf in a back room between two older clocks, who were busy ticking away the noisy seconds. "Well," said one of the clocks to the newcomer, "so you've started on this task; I'm sorry for you. You're ticking bravely now, but you'll be tired enough before you get through your thirty-three million ticks."

"Thirty-three million ticks!" said the frightened clock, "why I could never do that," and it instantly stood still with despair.

"Why you silly thing," said the other clock, "why do you listen to such words? It's nothing of the kind. You've only got to make one tick this moment; there, now, isn't that easy? And now another the next moment, and that is just as easy; and so right along."

"Oh, if that's all," cried the new clock, "that's easily done, so here I go," and started bravely on again, making a tick a moment, and not counting the minutes and months. But when the year was ended, it had made thirty-three million vibrations without knowing it.

ONE YEAR'S EXPERIENCE

At a boys' school, a new headmaster was chosen from among members of the faculty. After the appointment was announced, a teacher approached the chairman of the selection committee with a gnawing question.

"I accept the fact that I wasn't picked for the headmastership," he said forthrightly, "but can you tell me why I wasn't at least considered for the post? It seems curious. After all, I've had twenty years' teaching experience here."

"That's not quite the way we looked at it," came the reply. "In your case, the board felt that what you've had is *one* year's experience repeated twenty times.''

THE POWER OF A DOMINATING PURPOSE

Lincoln walked forty miles to borrow a book which he could not afford to buy.

Goethe spent his entire fortune of over half a million dollars on his education.

Milton wrote *Paradise Lost* in a world he could not see, and then sold it for fifteen pounds.

John Bunyan wrote *Pilgrim's Progress* in prison, at the urging of his conscience and in disregard of the orders of his accusers.

Carlyle, after lending the manuscript of the *French Revolution* to a friend, whose servant carelessly used it to kindle a fire, calmly went to work and rewrote it.

Cyrus W. Field risked a fortune and devoted years of seemingly hopeless drudgery, amid the scoffs of men, to lay the Atlantic cable.

Handel practiced on his harpsichord in secret, until every key was hollowed by his fingers to resemble the bowl of a spoon.

—Leaders of Men

PRESCRIPTIONS FOR LAZINESS

All physicians are not as frank as the doctor who, having been visited by the lazy man who complained of dyspepsia, gave him the following prescription:

"Take one wood saw and five cords of wood and saw the wood into fireplace lengths in three weeks."

Nor are they so frank as another doctor, who was visited by a lady who said that she was constantly troubled with loss of sleep, loss of appetite, and sluggishness.

The doctor wrote her a prescription. "Follow this faithfully," he said, "and you will be able to sleep and to eat, and will feel as brisk as a child at play."

The lady took the prescription and went out. She had scarcely reached the stairway before she opened and read it:

"Stop at the first shoe store you come to, buy six pairs of walking shoes, and wear them all out in three months."

A REASON FOR IDLENESS

When a young man was asked why he stayed in bed all day he answered, "Because every morning I have to listen to a debate. First Work gives me twenty reasons to get up. Then Laziness gives me twenty reasons to stay in bed. Then they argue back and forth. And by the time they're finished, it's time for dinner."

STICK TO YOUR BUSH

A rich man, in answer to the question of how he became so very successful, told the following story:

One day when I was a boy, a party of young girls and boys were going on an outing to pick blackberries. I wanted to go with them, but was afraid my father wouldn't let me, as he was so ill. When I told him what was going on, he gave me permission immediately to go. I was so excited I rushed to the kitchen and found a big basket, then asked mother to pack me a lunch. Just then my father called me back to him. When I went into his room he said, "Joseph, what are you going to do?"

"Pick berries," I replied.

"Then, Joseph, I want to tell you one thing: If you find a pretty good bush, do not leave it to seek a better one. The other boys and girls will run about, picking a little here and a little there, wasting a great deal of time and getting few berries."

I went on the outing and had a wonderful time. But it was just as my father had said it would be. No sooner had one boy found a good bush than he called all the rest, and they left their places to run off to the new bush. After a minute or two in one place, they rambled all over the pasture, getting tired and gathering few berries. I remembered my father's words and "stuck to the good bush" I had found. When I was done with it, I found another, and finished that, then I took another. When night came I had a large basket full of berries, more than all the others put together, and I was not half as tired as the other kids. I went home happy. When I arrived, I found my father more ill than ever. But when he looked at my basket full of ripe blackberries, he said, "Well done, Joseph. Wasn't I right when I told you to always stick to your bush?"

A short time after that incident, my father died. I had to make my own way in the world as best I could. But my father's words sank deep into my mind, and I never forgot the experience of the blackberry party; I "stuck to my bush." When I got a promising job and felt good about the quality of my work, I did not leave it and spend weeks and months seeking one a little better. When friends said, "Come with us, and we will make a fortune in a few weeks," I shook my head, and "stuck to my bush." After a while my employers offered to take me into the business as a partner. I continued to work and rise until I had principal control of the business. I was contented and had everything I wanted. The habit of sticking to my business led people to trust me, and gave me a character. I owe all I have and am to my father's motto: "Stick to your bush."

WHAT AN ERRAND BOY BECAME

John Campbell began life as an errand boy in a printing office. When he died he was worth a million dollars, and had been chief justice and lord chancellor of England. He was so long, lank, ungainly and awkward that an ordinary observer would have said, "That boy's place is to run errands, sweep floors and do general drudgery."

But his employer noticed that John, though dull and slow, was prompt and painstaking. When told to do anything, he went at it promptly and kept at it until the job was done.

The employer encouraged the dull, slow, but industrious boy and threw odd jobs in his way, by which he earned a little money. The boy had vigorous health and a strong body. Those, with his painstaking habit, were his sole capital. But they were sufficient.

WORK AND PRAY TOO

A doctor was once attending a poor woman in labor. It was a desperate case, requiring a cool head and a strong will. The good man—for he was good—had neither of these, and, losing his presence of mind, gave up the poor woman as lost and retired into the next room to pray for her. Another doctor, who perhaps did not have the first doctor's talent, but definitely had what the first doctor did not have—determination and courage—meanwhile arrived and called out, "Where is the doctor?"

"Oh, he's gone into the next room to pray!"

"Pray! Tell him to come here this moment and help me. He can work and pray too." And together they saved the woman's life.

A ZEALOUS WIFE

An enthusiastic wife was being lectured by her husband on her excessive exuberance. When her husband had finished his say, she replied, "I don't know about having too much zeal, but I believe it's better that the pot should boil over than to not boil at all."

THE HEIGHTS OF GREAT MEN

The heights by great men reached and kept
Were not attained by sudden flight;
But they, while their companions slept,
Were toiling upwards in the night.
—*Henry Wadsworth Longfellow*

LOST DAYS

The lost days of my life until today,
What were they, could I see them on the street
Lie as they fell? Would they be ears of wheat
Sown once for food but trodden into clay?
Or golden coins squandered and still to pay?
Or drops of blood dabbling the guilty feet?
Or such spilt water as in dreams must cheat
The undying thirst of Hell, athirst alway?

I do not see them here; but after death
God knows I know the faces I shall see,
Each one a murdered self, with low last breath,
"I am thyself,—what hast thou done to me?"
"And I—and I—thyself," (lo! each one saith,)
"And thou thyself to all eternity!"
—*Dante Gabriel Rossetti*

A PSALM OF LIFE

Tell me not, in mournful numbers,
Life is but an empty dream!
For the soul is dead that slumbers,
And things are not what they seem.

Life is real! Life is earnest!
And the grave is not its goal;
Dust thou art, to dust returnest,
Was not spoken of the soul.

Not enjoyment, and not sorrow,
Is our destined end or way;
But to act, that each tomorrow
Find us farther than today.

In the world's broad field of battle,
In the bivouac of Life,
Be not like dumb, driven cattle!
Be a hero in the strife!

Trust no Future, howe'er pleasant!
Let the dead Past bury its dead!
Act,—act in the living Present!
Heart within, and God o'erhead!

Lives of great men all remind us
We can make our lives sublime,
And, departing, leave behind us
Footprints on the sands of time;

Footprints, that perhaps another,
Sailing o'er life's solemn main,
A forlorn and shipwrecked brother
Seeing, shall take heart again.

Let us, then, be up and doing,
With a heart for any fate;
Still achieving, still pursuing,
Learn to labor and to wait.
                    —*Henry Wadsworth Longfellow*

THE SEEDLING

As a quiet little seedling
Lay within its darksome bed,
To itself it fell a-talking,
And this is what it said:

"I am not so very robust,
But I'll do the best I can";
And the seedling from that moment
Its work of life began.

So it pushed a little leaflet
Up into the light of day,
To examine the surroundings
And show the rest the way.

The leaflet liked the prospect,
So it called its brother, Stem;
Then two other leaflets heard it,
And quickly followed them.

To be sure, the haste and hurry
Made the seedling sweat and pant;
But almost before it knew it
It found itself a plant.

The sunshine poured upon it,
And the clouds they gave a shower;
And the little plant kept growing
Till it found itself a flower.

Little folks, be like the seedling,
Always do the best you can;
Every child must share life's labor
Just as well as every man.

And the sun and showers will help you
Through the lonesome, struggling hours;
Till you raise to light and beauty
Virtue's fair, unfading flowers.
                    —*Paul Laurence Dunbar*

WORK

Let me but do my work from day to day,
In field or forest, at the desk or loom,
In roaring market-place or tranquil room;
Let me but find it in my heart to say,
When vagrant wishes beckon me astray,
"This is my work; my blessing, not my doom;
"Of all who live, I am the one by whom
"This work can best be done in the right way."

Then shall I see it not too great, nor small,
To suit my spirit and to prove my powers;
Then shall I cheerfully greet the laboring hours,
And cheerfully turn, when the long shadows fall
At eventide, to play and love and rest,
Because I know for me my work is best.
                    —*Henry Van Dyke*

Author/Source Index

In this author/source index, references are separated by commas and designate page and item number. For example 9:3 is the third item that begins on page 9.

Subject/Title Index

In this subject/title index, subjects are shown in regular type, titles in italics. References are separated by commas and designate page and item number. For example, 9:3 is the third item that begins on page 9. The occasional use of a hyphen indicates subject spread on a series of pages; for example, Adversity, 1-7.

A

Abbot, Charles, 5:2
Ability, 59:5, 126:1
Abuse, 66:2, 67:1
Acceptance, 6:6, 83:3, 87:2, 87:3, 87:4, 109:2, 114:2, 124:2
Accomplices, 106:1
Accomplices in Sin, 106:1
Accomplishment, 26:4, 71:4
    See also Achievement
Accusations, 44:4
    See also Blame
Achievement, 60:2, 71:4
Acting, 65:1
Action, 65:1, 71:4, 129:6
    See also Work
Actions, 106:3, 116:4
Activity, 82:4
Adams, John, 112:5
Adapting, 125:5
Addiction, 33:1
    See also Habit; Word of Wisdom
Adjustment, 9:1
    See also Adapting
Adversity, 1-7, 41:2, 42:2, 71:7, 74:4, 94:2, 96:4, 124:2, 128:1
Advice, 52:5, 79:2, 102:5
Affection, 31:1, 66:4
    See also Love
Affliction, 87:3
    See also Adversity
Afterlife, 26:2
    See also Death
Age, 60:5, 62:6, 122:1
Agony, 104:1
    See also Pain
Aiming, 49:3
    See also Goals
Alcohol, 85:2, 118:1, 119:2, 119:3, 122:1, 122:2, 122:3, 123:1, 123:2
    See also Word of Wisdom
All the Way to Great Britain, 72:1
All Things Bright and Beautiful, 17:2
Allegory, An, 56:5
Alphabet Prayer, The, 20:1
Alphonsus, King, 100:6

Always Before My Eyes, 27:1
Always Look Up, 20:2
Ambition, 8:5, 11:2, 57:4
    See also Goals
America, 94:2
Amusement, 16:2
    See also Humor
Andrew Marvell and the Bribe, 43:1
Angels, 39:6, 54:2, 114:4
Anger, 3:1, 3:2, 4:4, 5:1, 5:3, 8:5, 16:1, 33:2, 43:3, 44:3, 53:3, 56:1, 64:4, 65:1, 66:1, 67:1, 85:3, 99:1, 102:2, 108:4
    See also Contention
Animals, 14:5, 15:1, 16:1, 16:2, 16:5, 20:3, 35:1, 51:1, 59:5, 64:3, 112:6, 121:1, 122:3
    See also Nature
Answers, 94:1, 96:1
Anticipation, 1:2
Antigonus, 78:2
Anxiety, 1:2, 93:1
Appearance, 51:1, 51:4, 52:1, 52:5, 53:3, 56:4
Appetite, 128:2
Appreciation, 77:4
    See also Worth
Approval, 26:4
Arabic Prescription for Sleeplessness, 124:1
Arabs, 9:1
Arcadius, 64:1
Arguing, 1:1, 70:1, 108:4, 114:1
    See also Contention
Aristippus, 8:5
Armor, 49:2
Art, 62:5
Art of Quarreling, The, 1:1
Art of Saying No, The, 27:2
As God Will, 87:3
Asa and Ira, 124:2
Ask Him, 90:1
Asking, 90:1, 95:3
Astronomer, 19:3
Atheism, 35:1, 39:3, 114:1, 115:4, 116:4
    See also God

Attention, 64:4, 66:4
Attitude, 1:3, 1:4, 3:3, 3:5, 4:4, 8:1, 9:1, 52:4, 53:3, 62:2, 69:3, 125:4
Audubon, John James, 57:5
Austerity, 64:4
Authority, 37:4, 46:4, 47:2
    See also Power
Autumn, 14:4
    See also Fall
Avoiding Conviction, 59:1
Awareness, 119:3
    See also Knowledge

B

Bacchus, Dr., 95:2
Bad, 34:2, 86:4
    See also Evil; Goodness
Bad Lump, The, 118:1
Banishment, 49:1
Bankrupt, 10:5
Baptism, 101:4
Bargain, 72:2
Barkeeper, 123:2
    See also Alcohol; Word of Wisdom
Bars, 85:2, 118:2, 123:2
    See also Alcohol; Barkeeper; Word of Wisdom
Battle, 66:1, 87:4, 129:6
    See also Contention
Be Strong, 87:4
Beating, 67:1
    See also Contention
Beauty, 11:3, 11:6, 12:3, 14:2, 14:3, 15:1, 15:3, 16:3, 16:4, 17:2, 17:3, 17:4, 17:5, 17:6, 17:7, 18:1, 18:2, 18:3, 18:4, 19:1, 19:2, 19:3, 26:1, 26:2, 26:3, 26:4, 30:2, 31:1, 35:3, 39:3, 40:4, 40:5, 41:1, 42:2, 50:3, 52:5, 54:2, 55:3, 55:5, 56:3, 98:5, 110:2, 104:3, 106:6, 114:3
Beecher, Henry Ward, 72:2
Bees, 7:1, 85:3, 114:3, 127:1
Begging, 77:3
    See also Charity
Behold the Fowls of the Air, 14:1

Mormon Tabernacle Choir, 37:3
Mortality, 84:3
  See also Life
Moses, 15:4
Mother, 5:4, 8:1, 20:4, 25:5, 27:2,
  27:3, 29:1, 29:3, 31:2, 31:4, 31:5,
  32:1, 32:2, 34:1, 34:2, 34:3, 34:5,
  36:4, 37:2, 44:3, 64:2, 68:1, 82:4,
  85:2, 87:1
  See also Family
Mother Beymer's Dividends, 31:4
Mother Never Told a Lie, 31:5
Mother's Jewels, A, 32:1
Mother's Name, A, 34:5
Motivation, 70:1
  See also Encouragement; Persuasion
Mountain, 17:2
Mr. Cobb's Covenant, 78:5
Mrs. Howard's Spending Money, 78:6
Murder, 14:5, 16:2, 16:4, 42:2, 48:1
  See also Killing
Murmuring, 87:3
  See also Criticism
Music, 4:2, 16:4, 18:4, 31:2, 37:3,
  38:4, 41:4, 52:4, 57:4, 59:3, 96:4,
  97:1, 97:2, 98:1
  See also Singing; Song
My Cigarette Money, 121:2
My Mother's Translation, 32:2
My Stick Is My Own, 67:1

N

Naive Versus Mature Faith, 21:3
Names, 57:1, 66:2
Napoleon, 3:4, 34:1
Nation, 49:4
National Education Association, 23:4
Nation's Strength, A, 49:4
Nature, 4:2, 7:1, 10:5, 11:1, 11:3,
  11:4, 11:6, 12:3, 14-19, 20:3, 21:3,
  24:2, 25:5, 25:6, 26:1, 26:2, 26:3,
  26:4, 30:2, 35:3, 36:3, 39:3, 40:1,
  40:4, 40:5, 41:1, 41:5, 42:2, 51:1,
  57:5, 59:5, 63:3, 68:3, 70:2, 71:2,
  88:2, 97:1, 97:2, 100:2, 100:4, 100:5,
  104:3, 105:1, 109:2, 112:6, 114:3,
  121:1, 122:3, 127:1, 130:1
  See also Earth
Nature and Miracles, 15:4
Nature of Patience, The, 127:4
Nature's Creed, 18:2
Need, 6:3, 65:2
Neighbors, 70:2
Never Too Old to Learn, 60:5
New Jerusalem, 72:2
New Orleans, Louisiana, 31:5
New Year, 57:4, 98:2
New Year Prayer, A, 98:2
New York, 1:4, 64:5
New Zealand, 80:5
Newton, Isaac, 51:4, 63:3, 127:4
Nick of Time, The, 32:3
Nightingale, 4:2

No Greater Love, 67:2
No Sweeter Thing, 41:4
Nobility, 4:4, 72:3, 89:2, 98:5
  See also Integrity
Noble Hospital, A, 102:1
Noise, 62:1
North and South, 67:3
Not a Penny, 46:3
Not Her Type of People, 106:6
Not in Vain, 12:2
Not Knowing Why, 63:2
Not Mine, but Thine, 6:5
Not Prepared for a Long Trip, 107:1
Not Rich but Generous, 79:1
Not Yet Old Enough to Need It, 122:1
Nourishment, 116:3
  See also Food

O

Obedience, 18:4, 20:4, 21:3, 22:1,
  23:1, 25:1, 25:2, 27:2, 33:2, 54:3,
  82-89, 97:3, 101:4, 102:5, 104:3,
  106:6, 107:3, 109:2, 109:5, 113:1,
  120:2
Oberlin, John Frederic, 80:1
Obscenity, 64:4
Obstinate, 85:1
  See also Obedience
Obstinate Citizens of Oudenarde, The,
  85:1
Oglethorpe, James Edward, 53:2
Oh Yet We Trust That Somehow Good,
  25:6
Old Jim, 16:1
Old Sack of Bones, The, 54:4
On the Setting Sun, 26:1
On the Twenty-third Psalm, 6:6
One Tick at a Time, 127:5
One World, 41:5
One Year's Experience, 127:5
Only One Fault, 122:2
Only Two, 74:3
Open-mindedness, 46:1
  See also Knowledge
Opportunity, 104:2
Opportunity, 110:2
Opposition, 2:1
  See also Adversity
Oppression, 44:4
  See also Adversity
Optimism, 8:1, 8:3, 9:1, 10:2, 66:1
  See also Pessimism
Originality, 51:4
  See also Creativity
Orthodoxy, 59:5
Others, 90:3, 98:4
  See also Charity; Love; Selflessness
Oudenarde, 85:1
Our Burden Bearer, 98:3
Our Father's World, 12:3
Out in the Fields with God, 7:1
Out with the Gentlemen, 85:2
Owl-Critic, The, 57:5

P

Page, Colonel, 103:1
Pain, 6:2, 6:4, 11:5, 12:2, 12:3, 12:5,
  12:6, 16:2, 41:2, 70:4, 87:3, 96:1,
  97:2, 104:1
  See also Adversity
Painting, 31:2, 55:6, 84:1
Panic, 2:1, 69:1
  See also Fear
Parable of the Owl Express, The, 22:1
Parable of the Unwise Bee, The, 85:3
Paradise Lost, 42:3, 128:1
Pardon, 47:2
  See also Forgiveness; Repentance
Parenthood, 28:2, 29:1, 29:3, 37:4
  See also Family
Parley P. Pratt and the Book of
  Mormon, 115:3
Parliament, 43:1
Passion, 64:4
Past, 109:6, 110:1, 110:3, 129:5, 129:6
  See also Future
Path, 24:3
Patience, 1:3, 3:1, 3:2, 3:3, 4:3, 5:3,
  5:4, 12:4, 16:1, 21:2, 22:1, 25:4,
  29:1, 32:3, 33:2, 52:4, 54:4, 66:1,
  74:1, 74:4, 101:1, 114:3, 127:4,
  129:6
  See also Perseverance
Patience in Trial, 74:4
Patriotism, 94:2
Patterns, 35:3
Payne, Mr., 108:4
Peace, 4:2, 7:1, 8:5, 11:1, 11:3, 11:5,
  12:4, 12:5, 16:1, 17:6, 18:4, 27:2,
  28:1, 39:6, 40:1, 41:1, 42:4, 50:3,
  57:4, 70:5, 86:4, 87:3, 89:1, 90:2,
  92:1, 93:1, 96:2, 96:3, 99:2, 99:3,
  100:1, 108:4, 112:2
  See also War
Peaceful Song, The, 4:2
Pedro, Dom, 102:1
Peer pressure, 106:4, 119:4
  See also Crowd following
Pennsylvania, 103:1
Perception, 17:5
  See also Understanding
Perfection, 31:3, 49:3
Pericles, 3:2
Peril, 56:1
  See also Adversity; Danger
Permanence, 113:1
Persecution, 54:4, 66:2, 74:4, 84:3,
  85:3
  See also Adversity
Perseverance, 1:3, 2:3, 4:3, 5:5, 6:1,
  6:3, 6:4, 6:5, 6:6, 7:2, 22:1, 23:3,
  33:3, 47:3, 48:2, 51:2, 61:1, 68:1,
  74:1, 87:4, 110:2, 126:3, 127:5,
  128:4, 129:1, 129:2, 129:4, 130:1
  See also Patience
Persistence, 126:3, 127:4, 128:4, 129:1
  See also Perseverance
Perspective, 1:4, 3:3, 4:1, 4:2, 5:1,